By Accid

Trevor Kletz was born in 1922 and educated at King's School, Chester and at Liverpool University during the Second World War. Inspired by the chance gift of a chemistry set when a boy of only eleven, he set off on a career in chemistry and chemical engineering. He joined ICI in 1944 as a research chemist at Yarm, 7 miles from Billingham, and spent 38 years with the company in the Teesside area. In 1952 he became a plant manager on Oil Works and, apart from two years planning and designing plants, moved from one works job to another, gaining operational and safety experience which served him well later. By 1961 he was assistant works manager.

In 1968 came a defining change of direction: appointed ICI's first technical safety adviser, for the next 14 years he hugely increased the scope and influence of the role and helped improve ICI's process safety record dramatically. Leaving ICI in 1982, Trevor Kletz made a second career as a consultant and prolific writer, commentator and lecturer on all aspects of process safety, travelling the world by invitation to pass on his wisdom. He has a long-standing association with the University of Loughborough (www.lboro.ac.uk/departments/cg/staff/cgtk.htm).

Elected a Fellow of the Institution of Chemical Engineers in 1978, to the Fellowship of Engineering (now the Royal Academy of Engineering) in 1984, and appointed an OBE for services to process safety in 1997, Trevor Kletz is the author of ten books and over a hundred papers on different aspects of process safety. He lives in Cheadle Hulme, Cheshire, UK.

By Accident...

...a life preventing them in industry

TREVOR KLETZ

First published 2000 by PFV Publications
Suite 5, 46 Islington Park Street, London N1 1PX, UK

ISBN 0-9538440-0-5

British Library Cataloguing-in-Publication Data
A catalogue record of this book is available from the British Library.

Typeset by Kathy Dean, Little Court Publishing, Exeter, UK
Printed and bound in Great Britain by Page Bros (Norwich) Ltd, Norfolk

CONTENTS

ALSO BY TREVOR KLETZ

Critical Aspects of Safety and Loss Prevention
(Butterworths 1990)

Lessons from Disaster
(IChemE 1993)

Learning from Accidents
(Butterworth-Heinemann, 2nd ed 1994)

Computer Control and Human Error
(IChemE, 1995)

Dispelling Chemical Engineering Myths
(Taylor & Francis, 3rd ed 1996)

What Went Wrong?
(Gulf, 4th ed 1998)

Process Plants: a Handbook of Inherently Safer Design
(Taylor & Francis, 2nd ed 1998)

Hazop and Hazan
(IChemE, 4th ed 1999)

An Engineer's View of Human Error
(IChemE, 3rd ed 2001)

ILLUSTRATIONS

Those not credited are reproduced by courtesy of ICI
Photos/illustrations from Trevor Kletz's private collection are marked (TK)
page x   Cartoon by Phlonce
page 9   Cartoon by Jim Watson
page 31 The one-legged stool

Section between pages 48 and 49
My maternal grandfather in the 1860s (TK);
A holiday sketch of me in 1946, aged 23 (TK)
Bill Price in the 1960s (King's College London); John Cullen, 1960s;
Bob Malpas, 1960s (Sir Robert Malpas)
Billingham Works Council, 1955; John Harvey-Jones, 1971
US Plant, 1952; Oil Works replacement plant after the 1957 fire
Acetone Plant Control Room, 1952
Acetone Plant distillation columns, 1950s
Oil Works tank fire, 1966; Tar Acids Plant control room, 1958
Conversion Section: a high pressure vessel; spanners for high pressure
vessels, 1960
James Woolcock, 1960s; Henry Simpson, early 1950s; Kenneth Gee,
about 1970
Rab Telfer and Sir Derek Ezra, 1978

Section between pages 80 and 81
Harland Frank, 1977; Edward Challis, 1973
Frank Lees, 1993 (Elizabeth Lees); Jim McQuaid, 1977
My wife Denise with our two boys, 1965 (TK)
My parents, the boys and me, 1969 (TK)
ICI's new technical safety adviser, 1968
ICI's Wilton site, 1974
Denise and me celebrating 35 years' service, 1979 (TK)
Me in my office at Billingham before the move to Wilton, 1974
Robed for my DSc at Loughborough, 1986 (TK)
OBE Insignia, 1997 (TK)
Opening the Astra Charnwood pilot plant, 1998 (AstraZeneca)

ACKNOWLEDGEMENTS

I would like to thank the many friends and former colleagues whose friendship, helpfulness and willingness to share information have made my career and this book possible; Sir John Harvey-Jones for writing a Foreword, Professor Michael Streat and Mr Jon Walker of Loughborough University for their help and encouragement and my editor, Dr Peter Varey, for his guidance and editorial skills.

The publication of this book was supported through a donation from Process R&D, AstraZeneca R&D, Charnwood.

I gave orders for my horse to be brought round from the stable. The servant did not understand me. I myself went to the stable, saddled my horse and mounted. In the distance I heard a bugle call, I asked him what this meant. He knew nothing and had heard nothing. At the gate he stopped me, asking: 'Where are you riding to, master?' 'I don't know,' I said, 'only away from here, away from here. Always away from here, only by doing so can I reach my destination.' 'And so you know your destination?' he asked. 'Yes,' I answered, 'didn't I say so? Away-From-Here, that is my destination.' 'You have no provisions with you,' he said. 'I need none,' I said, 'the journey is so long that I must die of hunger if I don't get anything on the way. No provisions can save me. For it is, fortunately, a truly immense journey.'

Franz Kafka, *The Departure*

FOREWORD

by Sir John Harvey Jones

I am delighted to provide an introduction to Trevor Kletz's autobiography because it gives me an opportunity to pay a public tribute to the remarkable and important contribution he has made to the safe operation of all types of process plant.

He and I shared early experiences in the 1960s — all the people and events he refers to also influenced my views and values fundamentally. We were lucky to have worked with and for some giants of men and to have learnt our craft in a company which respected the right to be different, gave us headroom and trusted us to pursue what we believed to be important and worthwhile. Trevor single-handedly taught us to look at the problems of safety in a different way and demonstrated the hazards we unwittingly ignored. I have never believed managers are entitled to risk the health of their people in the pursuit of profit. Moreover all experience shows that safe operations are efficient operations and vice versa. Many of our mistakes were the direct result of failing to foresee and prevent dangerous situations developing, and this in an industry with horrific inherent risks.

I spent the first 20 years of my life in the Royal Navy and, like every sailor, learnt from my earliest years that a good sailor was a safe sailor. There was never any excuse for short cuts or less-than-thorough procedures. Far from being admired, the macho risk taker was recognised as a threat to himself and all who sailed with him. In too many factories in my youth, the persistent application of tried and tested safety rules was looked upon as an excuse to slow things up or as a slightly old-womanish nagging on detail.

Trevor traces the evolution of his own thinking, which paralleled the experience of many of us. It is a tragedy that for so many the "safety" facts of life are only irreversibly drummed into them as a result of a major accident; that every major accident was foreseeable and preventable if only those in charge looked at their operations with a "safety eye". Managers pride themselves on their ability to improve productivity and reduce costs, and yet a tithe of the effort which is put into these operations would transform the safety and effectiveness of their plant and the lives of those for whom the managers are responsible.

Trevor is too modest to allow himself the praise which is his due for his abilities as a catalytic teacher. I never attended one of his sessions without coming away with a new realisation of potential hazards which I had hitherto ignored. Unfortunate experiences teach us all the potential consequences of lack of attention, but even then it comes as a shock to realise that the commonplace lack of good housekeeping can result in loss of life.

My proudest boast during my stint as chairman was that for the first time ever ICI worldwide managed two consecutive years without a single fatal accident. This for me far overshadowed the fact that in the same two years we made record profits. I hope that readers of his book will share my and Trevor's belief that we were fortunate enough to pursue careers that were fascinating, enjoyable and fun in their own right, coupled with the satisfaction of believing that we were doing something of value to our society and for our fellow men.

In our pursuit of wealth and our overvaluation of material success we seem to have lost sight of the fact that most of us are motivated by the desire to contribute something worthwhile to the world in which we live. Great wealth is achievable by only a few people and, from my experience, seldom brings the benefits expected of it. The ability to contribute to making the lot of others better is attainable by every one of us and brings with it satisfaction and reward of a different, but infinitely more valuable, kind.

Trevor Kletz will, I am sure, always sleep soundly at night, secure in the knowledge that his life and talents have not been wasted, but rather that his persistence, imagination and passion have saved countless numbers of his fellow men from injury, mutilation and even death. I salute him, and commend this book to you.

Sir John Harvey-Jones was Chairman of ICI from 1982 to 1987

INTRODUCTION

Everybody who is anybody in politics or show business (and a lot of people who are not even household names in their own households) feel compelled to write their memoirs. If you are contemplating a career as a politician or on the stage, you will have no difficulty finding out, in considerable detail, the sort of world you will enter and the sort of work you will do. In contrast, if you are contemplating a career as a chemical engineer or a chemist or any other kind of engineer, you will find it difficult to learn about the sort of life you will lead and the sort of things you will do, especially if there are few engineers or scientists among your friends and family.

Though many scientists have written autobiographies, there are very few by industrial chemists or engineers. The only recent books that I know of are *Well Oiled* by Alfie Wilson (Northgate Publishing, London, 1979) who describes his career in Shell in the period 1931-1962 and *High Speed Gas* by Sir Kenneth Hutchison (Duckworth, London, 1987), a former deputy chairman of the Gas Council whose experience came somewhat later. Both are well worth reading, especially the first as it is less descriptive and more analytic. Norman Swindin's *Engineering Without Wheels* (Weidenfeld and Nicolson, London, 1962, 1978) is outstanding, but it covers a period now long past (he was born in 1880) and he was an outstanding man, whom few can hope to emulate.

I therefore thought that a short account of my career might be of interest. By a providential accident I was in the right place at the right time to take part in the revolution in our attitude to process safety that took place from the late 1960s onwards. I try to convey the excitement of the time and the book should therefore interest all those who wish to know how the growth of loss prevention came about. Many of the lessons I learned apply to other forms of innovation and may therefore attract all those interested in the mechanism of innovation as well as engineers and safety advisers.

Another reason for writing this book is that it provides a view of industry from within — there are many descriptions of it from the top and from the outside (by sociologists, a few of whom I quote) but few by middle managers.

I also aim to give students at school or university who are considering chemistry or chemical engineering or indeed any branch of engineering as a career, and those who advise them, an idea of what to expect. I hope the book will show them that life in industry is useful, satisfying and enjoyable. It is useful because it contributes to the wealth of the nation and the world. It is satisfying because it is concerned with the solving of stimulating problems in an environment where the necessary resources are usually available — making the best of those that are available is sometimes part of the challenge. It is enjoyable because you work in co-operation with colleagues who are usually helpful and pleasant to work with. Not all companies are the same but in ICI there were very few people who were prepared to trample on others in order get on. I can think of only three that I knew.

I joined ICI in 1944, and retired from the company in 1982, so my recollections are not recent. But while economic situations and equipment designs change, people remain the same, and they have more influence on the culture of a company than the design of plant and equipment.

Also plant designs do not change all that quickly. There was equipment still in use at Billingham when I retired that was installed when I was at school. The biggest changes have been in methods of control. When I joined the company most plants were still hand-controlled. When I retired computer control was being introduced on most new and some old plants. Today it is standard and more sophisticated. But as I show in my book on *Computer Control and Human Error* (Kletz T A, Chung P W H, Broomfield E and Shen-Orr C, Institution of Chemical Engineers, Rugby, 1995), computer control has provided new opportunities for familiar errors. Nevertheless, I have given more technical detail for the latter part of my career, when I was involved full-time in loss prevention.

Many of the brightest people of my generation were attracted to industry but since then its reputation has fallen, for various reasons. There was a period when many were attracted to jobs through which they felt they could help their fellow men and women. For example, in a broadcast some years ago, John Garnett, a former ICI personnel manager and a writer and consultant on industrial relations, described a conversation with some students who had hitch-hiked a lift with him. When they graduated, they said, they wanted a socially useful job, such as allocating council houses. He asked them if they had considered a career in which they created more wealth instead of allocating more fairly the wealth that was already available. The question surprised them; they admitted they had not looked at things in this way before.

More recently, many young people have been attracted to the City and other financial services where earnings are higher than those of engineers and chemists. But the grass on the other side always looks greener. It is easy to find examples of people who earn more than engineers, but beware of comparing the median pay of engineers with top salaries elsewhere. Also, some of the wealth of City people is paper money, such as options whose value can shrink or disappear overnight.

More important, perhaps, is a fear that industry is a dull and soulless grind. There are still many who feel like Seneca (4 BC-65 AD):

But the inventing of such things (as glass) is drudgery for the lowest of slaves; philosophy lies deeper. It is not his office to teach men how to use their hands. The object of his lessons is to form the soul.
(Quoted by MacKay A L, *The Harvest of the Quiet Eye*, Institute of Physics, Bristol, 1977, p135)

Alfie Wilson (page 48 of reference on page xiii) quotes an essay by a sixth-form student, no different from what one sees today:

To me industry appears deadening, an unending treadmill. The human being is converted into a cog in some massive industrial machine, and a very small cog at that... The pursuit of what I shall call "spiritual awards" is the new burning issue in choosing a career — hence the growth of the public sector "non-producers" such as teachers, social workers, even those much maligned public servants, the Civil Service... I am looking for these very "spiritual awards", something which industry, at the moment, cannot, or will not, supply.

On 30 November 1985 the *Daily Telegraph* reported the results of a survey of Britain's school children. The brightest children, it reported, regarded working in industry as boring and routine and as making little contribution to the country's well-being. It rarely provided worthwhile careers and was the last thing their fathers and mothers wanted them to work in. "There was no significant understanding among the schoolchildren of the importance of business as the basis of wealth creation." This is still true.

There is also a belief that industry is responsible for pollution of the environment. Many do not realise that industry, and the chemical industry in particular, provides the necessities for our modern way of life. In fact service industries, including financial, medical and social services, are only made possible by the wealth-producing activities of industry, and the environment is far cleaner than it was in my youth.

I shall try to show that industry can supply the "spiritual awards" that Alfie Wilson's sixth-former wants as well as creating the wealth that allows the "non-producers" to make their contribution.

My private life has been relatively uneventful so I give only a brief account of it, just enough to show the manner of man that I am. Some engineers, such as Alfie Wilson, are very extrovert but you do not have to be like that to succeed. I have never been a great enthusiast for a night out with the boys and I still find cocktail-party talk difficult. Perhaps introverts have the advantage that they are less distracted by the demands of social life.

If there are occasional criticisms of my old company, ICI, in this book, they are the criticisms of a friend. Throughout my career and following my retirement ICI treated me fairly, even generously. The company had its weaknesses but they were far outweighed by its virtues. The Appendix to Chapter 9 on page 123 is an article I wrote for the *ICI Magazine* after retiring. I write in the past tense about the company as it has changed much more in the 18 years since I left than in the 38 years I was there.

I use the terms process safety and loss prevention interchangeably to indicate the scientific study of safety. United States readers should note that in the United Kingdom a plant manager is the first level of professional management, someone who would be called a supervisor in most US companies. A supervisor in the UK is another name for a foreman or someone of equivalent rank.

Cheadle Hulme, May 2000

1

EARLY YEARS

Look to the rock from which you were hewn,
and the quarry from which you were cut

Isaiah 51:1

I was born in 1922 in Darlington, in the North of England, the eldest of three children, to orthodox but anglicised Jewish parents (and though far from orthodox I have remained within the Jewish community). My family moved to Coventry and then to Chester, where I spent my formative years and which I look on as my hometown.

Examinations

I first went to small private schools, sometimes called dame schools, and then to the local primary school, or elementary school as it was then called. In 1933, at the age of 10, I had to sit an examination to decide whether I stayed on at the elementary school until 14 and then started work (as my father had done), or whether I transferred to a local grammar school. The exam was in two parts. The first was held at my school and, having passed this hurdle, I had to attend one of the local grammar schools to sit the second part. We were then sent into the playground while the papers were marked.

When we were called back into the school the examiner said that 27 had passed and he would read out their names, starting with that of the boy with the highest marks. I vividly remember counting the names on my fingers. I did not expect to be in the first 10 but by number 20 I was getting worried. I was number 27!

I have often wondered how my career would have developed if I had been number 28. I would have been allowed another try, as my father — though not wealthy — earned enough to have to pay the grammar school fees, and fee-payers were allowed a second try at an allegedly easier examination. However, as a result of my experience I have always favoured the principle of comprehensive education rather than selection at age 10 or 11. My Loughborough University colleague, Professor Gordon Wray FRS, actually failed the grammar school entrance examination and started work as an engineering apprentice. He studied for his Higher National Certificate in the evenings and started at university when he was 23.

The examination results seem to have been a fair estimate of my ability at the time. I went to the King's School, Chester and for a few years was at, or near, the bottom of the form. Gradually I worked my way up, helped by the increasing contribution of physics and chemistry, my best subjects, and ended up as head boy. Several boys, better qualified than I was, left early because of the war, and so I quickly learnt that one way to get on is to hang around after others have left. Having said that, it is usually experience that counts, not seniority. In the sixth form we could study science, classics or moderns (history and French). I was one of the first head boys from the science sixth. Most of those who came before me, though not those who came later, had taken classics or moderns.

I had no problem deciding what career to follow. When I was 11 years old an uncle gave me a chemistry set and from then on I knew I wanted to be a chemist. At the time few people had heard of chemical engineering, the profession I actually moved into later. Nor was it difficult to decide which university to attend. In those days, if you were not good enough for Oxbridge, it was taken for granted that you would go to the local university. Halls of residence were for people who lived beyond daily travelling distance from any university. So in 1941 I started at the University of Liverpool.

Family background

My experience was typical of the grandchildren of the Jewish immigrants who emigrated from Russia to Britain in the late 19th century.

My paternal grandfather came to Britain in the 1880s from Lithuania, then part of Russia, and my father was born a few year later in 1891, the youngest of nine children. His generation left school as soon as they were allowed to and had make their way in the world. My generation aimed for university and disappointed their parents if they did not make it. The downside was frequent parental nagging to do better at school. I sometimes wonder if the pressure to do better is the reason why I have continued to work into my old age. But I think the enjoyment I get from the work is more important.

My maternal grandfather came to England somewhat earlier, in the 1860s. He was a rabbi in Warsaw when Sir Moses Montefiore, a Victorian philanthropist, founded a college near his home in Ramsgate in memory of his wife. It was primarily a community of scholars, though there were never more than four, rather than a teaching establishment, and my grandfather was one of the first group. His salary was £2 per week plus a house. I don't know whether he applied for the job or was headhunted.

He was born in 1824, when Beethoven was still alive, and he came to England as a widower with three grown-up daughters. He married a girl about the same age as his youngest daughter and fathered another nine children of whom my mother, born in 1892 when he was 68, was the youngest. She lived to be 99, so from her father's birth to her own death was 168 years.

Apart, perhaps, from greater pressure to do well at school, I had a typical middle class childhood of the period. My father earned, as a shop manager, about £10 per week — enough for a small semi-detached house in a nice suburb and some domestic help but not enough for a car, telephone or much in the way of holidays. (Only two people in the street had a car and one of them was a taxi-driver who owned his own vehicle). In the summer we sometimes went to Rhyl, a seaside town on the north coast of Wales, about 30 miles away but more often I was dispatched to stay with some of my numerous relatives for a couple of weeks. On returning to school in September some boys described holidays in France while I had been to Doncaster or Hartlepool. I never felt deprived or embarrassed. It never occurred to me that these places were not holiday resorts. And in other years I went to Edinburgh or Belfast.

University days

World War II started in September 1939 when I was still at school. When Hitler invaded Poland the Chamberlain government felt obliged to honour the promises it had made to protect that country. For six months nothing much happened; it was called the "phoney war". In the Spring of 1940 Hitler rapidly overran Norway and Denmark, followed by France and Benelux and the war started in earnest. I left school in 1941 and wanted to join the army, but my father and headmaster persuaded me that scientists were wanted more than soldiers. Government bursaries — worth far more than the local authority scholarship for which I had worked so hard — became available for anyone who could pass the minimum entrance requirements.

University in wartime was not much fun. There was little social life and most of that I missed as I travelled daily by train from Chester. An extra term was squeezed into the second summer vacation to shorten the course. Membership of the Senior Training Corps was compulsory. We spent two half-days per week on military training. It was the last organisation I would have joined voluntarily in peacetime, but to my surprise I found it on the whole very enjoyable and ended up as a cadet sergeant. I had joined the Home Guard (Dad's Army) in 1940 and this gave me my first experience of mixing with men of all types and ages. It was a man's world but it was a good preparation for my time as an ICI plant manager.

I found at the University that most of my fellow students had a narrower range of interests than most of the boys I had known at school where an interest in many subjects was encouraged. We had, for example, during our last two years, to write essays on many varied subjects. We take what we have been exposed to as the norm and it never occurred to me when I was at school that other grammar schools might be different. In the same way, I thought Chester was similar to other towns of the same size. The industrial North East (see Chapter 2) came as a shock.

At university we had lectures from Joseph Rotblat, then working on the atomic bomb project, who described nuclear fission. We did not realise that he was telling us anything out of the ordinary or that it was not in every chemistry syllabus. As his colleague Otto Frisch has related, "Rotblat even included fission in his lectures and mentioned the possibility of a chain reaction, but in such a casual way that nobody would have thought that it might lead to an important development in weaponry, let alone that we were actually working on that" (Frisch O R, *What Little I Remember*, Cambridge University Press, 1979, p142).

Choosing a career

I graduated in 1944. Rather than hang around at the University waiting for the results of the final examinations to be posted, a friend and I went on a cycling trip and I vividly remember arriving at Llanrwst Youth Hostel in North Wales and being handed a telegram. It was good news (firsts) for both of us. My companion on that trip, Harold Fore, has remained a lifelong friend and walking companion and I still go walking with him and his wife June.

I had the sort of inclinations which, in normal times, would have led me to stay on at University after graduating and work for a PhD. This was impossible in war-time and I looked for a job. They were easy to find and the "milk round" produced three offers: from the Royal Aircraft Establishment at Farnborough, from ICI Dyestuffs Division in Manchester and from ICI Billingham Division in the North-East of England. I found it hard to choose between the last two. I was impressed by the fact that at Billingham I had lunched with the Research Director while at Dyestuffs I had eaten in the canteen with a personnel officer. I was even more impressed by the view of the Billingham factory through the West Gate: ugly, frightening but challenging. But I was offered a job in research, not in the factory, and imagined myself spending my days at a laboratory bench, pouring things into test tubes. I don't think I have touched one since I left university.

As sometimes happens when a decision is difficult, it was made for me. I got a letter from the Royal Aircraft Establishment to say I had been allocated to them by the Ministry of Labour. I wrote to both ICI Divisions. Dyestuffs replied saying, in effect, "Hard luck". Billingham, in contrast, said, "Don't you believe it. You are free to choose." So on Monday 15 May 1944 I left home, walking to the station with my suitcase balanced on my bicycle. The elder of my two sisters came to see me off and the next day I started work at Billingham.

When my own sons left home to start work, about 40 years later, they drove off in their cars.

2

RESEARCH DAYS

Per Ardua ad Spectra

with apologies to the Royal Air Force

The company that I joined was very different to today's ICI. Formed in 1926 by the amalgamation of the country's four largest chemical companies, it was one of Britain's largest companies and one of the four largest chemical companies in the world. It was considered a sort of national institution. At its peak in the 1970s it employed 120,000 people in the United Kingdom, including about 10,000 at Billingham and a similar number at Wilton, 10 miles away on the other side of the River Tees. (At the end of 1999 there were 10,000 people in the entire company but 80,000 pensioners). In those days to join it was considered an achievement. With your appointment came the knowledge that, if you behaved yourself, you had a job until you were 62 and a pension thereafter. To leave without good reason was looked upon as foolish and almost disloyal. Chapter 9 describes some of the changes that took place just before and after I retired.

Infra-red spectroscopy

On arrival in May 1944 I was assigned to the "Tube Alloys" Section of the Research Department, which was carrying out contract work in connection with the production of the atomic bomb, and for a few weeks I worked under the supervision of Maurice Hodgson. Later (as Sir

Maurice Hodgson) he was chairman of the company. Before the war all the chemists recruited by ICI had a PhD or equivalent. Such people were not available in wartime so, to give new recruits some experience in research techniques, we worked for our first couple of years as assistants to a more experienced chemist.

It is an indication of the ability of the staff at ICI at the time I joined, and for many year afterwards — at least at Billingham — that besides Maurice, three other people that I worked with (Robert Malpas, John Cullen and John Harvey-Jones) were later knighted. Since I left ICI in 1982 I have increasingly felt the need to say that all management systems and all safety techniques are useless unless the people using them have knowledge, experience and ability.

After a few weeks I was transferred to the Physico-Chemical Section which was located in a small laboratory at Yarm, a country town about seven miles from Billingham. Here I was employed on infra-red spectroscopy with Bill Price, the first of a number of exceptionally capable men it has been my good fortune to work under. About Bill, and about several of the others I worked with in those days, I felt like Sir Isaac Newton: "If I have seen further it is by standing on the shoulders of giants".

Bill was the best experimental spectroscopist of his generation. He had left Cambridge to contribute to the war effort at Billingham, and it was a privilege to be able to work with him. I would not have done as well if I had been able to stay on at Liverpool to carry out research there. At the time infra-red spectroscopy was just coming into use, as a tool for analysis and for the determination of molecular structure, and we had to build or modify much of our apparatus. One of our principal jobs was the analysis of aviation fuel to determine the concentrations of various octane isomers. The composition had a big effect on performance.

Bill Price taught me to use my hands — something I had never learnt as a boy, as my father was not a do-it-yourself enthusiast, and at elementary school woodwork was for the non-academic only. I never became an experimentalist in the same class as Bill Price, but I did achieve a reasonable competence and this increased my self-confidence. Away from the Billingham factory we were able to ignore the restrictions on the use of tools that the trade unions normally imposed on laboratory staff. Bill also taught me not to pay too much attention to red tape. When the telephone lead was too short, he did not send for the telephone engineer, as required by the telephone company's rules, he just lengthened it himself.

A visit to Cambridge

Bill Price's expertise was ultra-violet rather than infra-red spectroscopy so I was sent to Cambridge for a month to learn more about infra-red techniques at Gordon Sutherland's laboratory. This was great fun. Cambridge seemed much less affected by the War than Liverpool and Gordon's research team were very helpful. Today a young graduate on company business expects a four-star hotel. I was told to look for student digs and was surprised to find the toilet at the bottom of the garden. I got £30 for the month's expenses and handed back a couple of pounds when I returned, even though I took Gordon's research team out for a meal the evening before I left.

Bill Price was also assisted by another young chemist, Douglas Wilson, who worked on ultra-violet spectroscopy. Douglas has remained a life-long friend.

The work at Yarm was idyllic in many ways. I was not working in a factory, but out in the country: one of a small team, carrying out fascinating work under the supervision of an outstanding teacher, with opportunity for growth, achievement, responsibility and recognition, qualities that I was later to recognise as necessary for job satisfaction (see Chapter 6). Many academics have a tendency to pooh-pooh research in industry but it can be just as satisfying as academic research so long as you are interested in practical goals. And it can be much more efficient, as less time is wasted writing interminable applications for grants. Bill and I were able to publish some of the work we did and I became sufficiently well known in the (small) infra-red field to be asked to referee papers.

People and relationships

The only fly in the ointment at Yarm was the section head. Throughout my time in ICI I came across very few incompetent people and very few unpleasant people, but he was the most incompetent and the most unpleasant. The incompetence hardly mattered; he did not know enough to interfere and left us alone technically. The unpleasantness just had to be borne. Even in those early days I sensed that this man was not typical of the company and that I should not judge it by him.

Throughout my time with the company the different ICI Divisions had markedly different cultures, derived from the characters of the founding companies. When, some years later, the Alkali Division (based in Northwich), which recruited mainly from Oxbridge, was merged with the more redbrick and working-class General Chemicals (based in Runcorn) to form Mond Division, a colleague remarked that there had been no similar merger since the Parliamentary Commissioners joined Eton and Slough.

Peter Allen, later company chairman, has described the cultural shock of moving from the Oxbridge atmosphere of Alkali Division to Dyestuffs, where "in the canteen men who have known each other for

30 years would say, 'May I trouble you for the salt, Dr Brown?' After work they went home to 'high tea'" (Reader W J, *Imperial Chemical Industries — A History*, Vol 2, OUP, Oxford, 1975, p72).

The most distinguished member of the Physico-Chemical Section was our mathematician, C H Bosanquet, an eccentric but capable and likeable man. In those days people were addressed by their surnames (prefixed by Mr if they were senior or much older) and only personal friends or very close colleagues were called by their first names — people who would be addressed as *tu* rather than *vous* in France. We knew that Bosanquet was Claude only because Douglas Wilson once said to him, "After you, Claude" (a Ted Kavanagh catchphrase from a popular radio show, ITMA or It's That Man Again) and got the surprised reply, "How did you know my name was Claude?"

A few weeks after my arrival at Yarm an incident showed me the pitfalls that await the unwary in large organisations. Price and the section head were both away when a light bulb in our equipment failed. It was an unusual type and I found we had no spare. I telephoned several local suppliers without success. A colleague suggested I try the Supply Department, whose job it was to get such things. I telephoned them — they were located some miles away — and put my problem to the girl who answered the phone. Perhaps I had overstressed its importance because she put me through to the head of the department, though I did not realise this. In order to show that I was not bothering him unnecessarily I described the efforts I had already made to find a bulb. His response shocked me. He lost his temper. Buying equipment was his job. If I started to do it myself I could damn well finish it myself. He was having nothing to do with it.

I sent a telegram to Bill Price, who was visiting Cambridge, and he got some bulbs there. The incident reinforced what I was learning: be self-reliant and solve problems yourself when you can.

Training in the factory
In 1946, after two years' experience, I became a full-blown "chemist" and was sent on a three-month training course to learn more about the Division. The first two months were spent on the Water Gas Plant, to give me some factory experience. In this plant steam was passed over red-hot coke to produce a mixture of hydrogen and carbon monoxide

(see Figure 2.1, page 13). I spent six weeks on the 2.00 pm to 10.00 pm shift, six days per week, as it was considered the best shift for training. In the mornings foremen and chargehands were too busy to give a trainee much attention and no-one is at their best during the night shift. I spent a few shifts with the general foremen (in charge of a wider area), a few with the Water Gas Plant foremen and a few more with the various chargehands and operators. It gave me a good insight into the operation of a plant which contained very little automation and which was hot, dirty, draughty and labour-intensive. Finally, in my last two weeks, I was given a small problem to investigate.

I cannot honestly say I enjoyed the experience. I was often bored, often dirty (I had worked on farms during school holidays but industrial dirt is more objectionable than agricultural dirt), often tired and often, I think, suffering from the effects of small doses of carbon monoxide. But it was worthwhile and I was grateful for the plant experience. Not only did I get an insight into the organisation and workings of the factory but it was good experience to mix with the process workers. I found that everyone from manager down to process worker went out of their way to be helpful.

The facts of life

I soon discovered that the process workers were much more than unskilled labourers. Later, however, I realised that most were ignorant of all but the essential knowledge of their jobs (that is, the minimum they had to know to be able to do them) and that they received no encouragement to find out more. More knowledge of the reasons for some of the readings, I thought, might lead to more care in adjusting and reading instruments. In the 1940s and later, promotion was often based on length of service rather than ability. In later years I was able to do a little to change these attitudes.

Chargehands got very little pay for their extra responsibility: they took all the decisions and sorted out all the problems. For a 48 hour week (8 hours per day, 6 days per week), including shift allowance, process workers earned between £5-18-8 (£5.94) and £6-5-4 (£6.27) per week while chargehands earned £6-8-0 (£6.40) to £6-19-8 (£6.97). For comparison I was earning £8.63 per week.

ICI had a good reputation for the way it treated employees at all levels but weekly-paid employees (known as payroll) were treated less generously than salaried staff. Foreman, though staff, were in between. Thus foremen were demoted if surplus, while other jobs were found for surplus salaried staff. Of course, conditions varied between departments depending on the attitude of the manager; many process workers could get a day off with pay more easily than I could at Yarm.

Since 1946 conditions of employment for payroll and staff have tended to converge. Everyone expected that payroll would get staff conditions but in the event the opposite has occurred. Professional staff in ICI and other companies now have less security of employment than ICI payroll had half a century ago.

Working hours had recently been reduced from 56 hours (seven shifts) per week to 48 hours (six shifts), so they did not seem too bad. On the 56-hour system there was never a day off. On a so-called long weekend men finished at 12.30 pm Saturday and returned at 10.00 pm Sunday. To earn that they had to do a quick return on the other two weekends, that is, finish at 6.00 am on Saturday and return at 12.30 pm, or finish at 10.00 pm Saturday and return at 6.00 am Sunday.

Water gas in context

The Water Gas Plant was in the mainstream of the Billingham factory, established by Brunner Mond after the First World War to manufacture synthetic ammonia by the Haber process and to convert much of it into fertilisers (Reader W J, *Imperial Chemical Industries — A History*, Vol 1, OUP, Oxford, 1975, p347). Coal from the Durham coalfields was converted to coke in the coke ovens and then moved to the water gas generators where it was heated by passing air through it (the blow cycle). Steam was then passed through the hot coke to produce water gas, a mixture of hydrogen and carbon monoxide (the make cycle). The gas was compressed and passed to the Hydrogen Plant where it reacted with more steam over a catalyst to produce carbon dioxide and more hydrogen. The gas then passed to the Ammonia Plant where it was compressed to a high pressure, carbon dioxide and residual carbon monoxide were removed and the hydrogen used for ammonia production. The nitrogen needed was obtained from the air used to heat the coke during the blow cycle (see Figure 2.1). A complex series of mechanically and hydraulically operated valves controlled the change-over

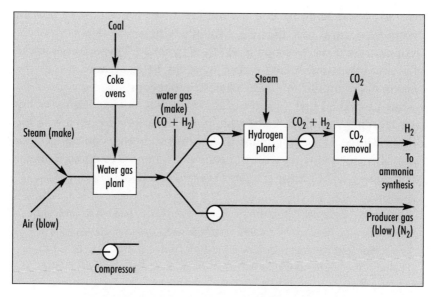

Figure 2.1: The Gas Section, ICI Billingham in 1946

between the make and blow cycles and the disposal of the exit gas (which could go to the hydrogen stream, to the nitrogen stream or to the stack). The operators' jobs were hot and dirty, and removing the ash from the generators was particularly unpleasant. Men stood in railway trucks and rodded the bases of the reactors until the ash fell out in a cloud of dust.

I spent the last month of the training course touring the departments together with another trainee. Some departments explained their work in comprehensive and painful detail (the Labour Department was the worst). In contrast, when we saw the head of the Catalyst Section at 9.00 am, he said, "We have set ourselves up to be the catalyst experts of the Division. More than that you do not need to know. Good morning." At 9.01 we were free to spend the rest of the day in the library.

Back to the infra-red

When the training programme was complete I was sent to a different section of the research department, to understudy the Division's expert on distillation. After a few days I went off on my annual holiday. When I returned I discovered that Bill Price was off to the United States for a year and I was to go back to my old job. I had a magnificent year in prospect, for I was now the infra-red king, with a great deal of freedom to run infra-red spectroscopy research as I wanted. I experienced, more than any other time in my career, what Sir Peter Medawar, calls the "exploratory impulsion" and "restless endeavour" of the committed research worker. I had a couple of assistants but still spent most of my time working with them in the laboratory. I have never agreed with the official ICI (or, at least Billingham Division) view that one can do first class experimental work with someone else's hands. To quote Sir Peter Medawar again (*Advice to a Young Scientist*, Pan Books, 1981, p11):

> Another scientifically disabling belief is to expect to be able to carry out experimental research by issuing instructions to lesser mortals who scurry hither and thither to do one's bidding. What is disabling about the belief is the failure to realise that experimentation is a form of thinking...

Similarly, as I was to find out later, managers and senior safety advisers cannot ask someone to read accident reports on their behalf and draw their attention to significant messages. They should read a substantial proportion themselves and visit the scene, as this is the only way to get a feel for the sort of incidents that are occurring and why they occur.

Things look up

The unpleasant head of section became more bearable and in any case left us alone so far as the work was concerned. Then, during the year, the research director retired, and his successor, Ronald Holroyd (later Sir Ronald) lost no time in moving the section head to a lone-worker job (he soon left the company) and appointing David Lees as section manager in his place. Though Lees was not, and would not have claimed to be, an outstanding scientist, he was a competent administrator and a straightforward, pleasant man and after his predecessor it was a pleasure to work with him. At the same time the Research Department was re-organised and a new layer of group managers were introduced between the research director and the section managers. We became part of the Physical Chemistry Group whose manager, Bernard Bradford, took a good deal of interest in our work. The accepted wisdom then was that extra layers of management improved efficiency.

The most fascinating parts of the job were developing the apparatus and using the results to unravel molecular structure. The analytical work was straightforward bread and butter stuff. The spectrometers used rocksalt prisms and sample cells as glass is opaque to infra-red rays. The prisms and cells had to be handled with great care. We had to keep the humidity low and touch nothing with our bare fingers. Spectra were recorded either photographically by a beam of light on a moving sheet of photographic paper or, later, by a pen recorder. From the strength and wavelength of the absorption bands we tried to puzzle out molecular structure, a sort of detective game.

We often had components made in the factory instrument workshop where the workmanship was first-rate. If a stand was made from a rod and cylinder, the two fitted like a piston in an engine cylinder. Then one day, a few years later, the workmanship suddenly fell off. The workshop had gone onto a bonus scheme, based on output. At first I was disappointed but then I realised that workmanship should be adequate, not perfect, and that the customer should define the quality required. Professional men, like craftsmen, often take a pride in the quality of their work and are reluctant to produce anything but the best, but in doing so they may take the client — or their employer — for a ride.

Odd job man

In October 1947 Bill Price returned from the United States but left again after a year to become a professor of physics at King's College, London. Soon after his return I was taken off infra-red spectroscopy and made the odd job man of the section. I was somewhat disappointed but on the other hand I could see the advantage of widening my experience. (Lees told me that in ICI anyone who gets more responsibility than normal for his age and service is soon put back in his place. It was not altogether true, but it was what Lees thought should happen.)

I built and used apparatus for measuring various physical properties such as magnetic susceptibility and differential refractometry. I have long forgotten of what use these properties were or how they were measured. The scrappy nature of the work made it difficult to be as interested as I had been in infra-red spectroscopy and this was the least exciting period in my whole ICI career. I felt I was stagnating in a well-paid, pleasant, undemanding rut and even started looking around for another job.

By Accident

The research director saw all the technical staff every December, when he informed them of their year-end salary rise and discussed their prospects. In December 1947 I had told him that I wanted to remain a researcher. He tried to dissuade me. A year later I was less certain and during 1950 I became sure that I had had enough of research — at least, as it was done at Billingham. Escape was not easy, however, as I was now working on one of Bradford's hobby horses: the measurement of infra-red spectra of very small samples, such as biological samples, using a reflecting microscope. In a diary note written at the end of 1950 I complained:

> I have tried to make my colleagues do some of the things I think worthwhile but without success; it is most discouraging. My ideas get listened to and ignored while Bradford's mad schemes get taken up. Lees is most cynical and scathing about the foolishness and uselessness of Bradford's ideas. Since the section moved to Billingham in the Spring he has become one of the lads instead of the rather aloof chief that he was.

I do not quote this to suggest that Bradford was wrong and that Lees and I were right (I may not have been) but to show that a worm's eye view (Lees' and mine) can be very different from a bird's eye view. Bradford was highly regarded and went on to have a successful career as a Division director.

All the same, the work on the infra-red spectra of small samples was 25 years before its time. It lay dormant until the late 1970s (Wetzel DL and Reffner JA, *Chemistry and Industry*, No 9, 8 May 2000, p308).

The work was interesting despite my reservations about its usefulness. On Monday mornings I felt I was wasting my time but by Friday I was caught up in the excitement of problem solving. For this reason it was not until December 1950 that I told Holroyd that I definitely wanted to leave research. He said that was wise and agreed to arrange it, but it took another year, during which I paid frequent visits to see his deputy to ask when the move would occur. Finally, I was told that I was to be transferred to the Oil Works on 1 January 1952 (New Year's Day was a working day then). At the age of 29 I felt I was about to put the playthings of youth behind me and join the real world. In contrast, Bradford said he hoped to see me back in Research Department as a section manager.

Away from work

When I started work in 1944 I stayed three nights in a hotel (for the first time in my life) and then moved into lodgings, the normal practice for single people working away from home at the time. Four years later ICI opened a hostel for unmarried professional men and I moved there. It was a great improvement. There was a good social life and I made many friends with whom went walking (or less often cycling) on weekends and holidays. Walking has been my main exercise as I have always been pretty hopeless at games. I count myself fortunate that I have always lived near good walking country and that, starting the new millennium at the age of 77, I can still enjoy days on the moors. It is the most relaxing activity I know: I forget completely about work, domestic problems and everything else.

Another advantage of the hostel was that expert advice was available on every conceivable topic: hi-fi, holiday destinations and, most important of all, car maintenance. I bought my first car in 1951, a 1935 Austin 10, and I think I spent more weekends working on it than driving it. The downside of the hostel was that after a few drinks a group of men — professional men in their twenties and early thirties — became schoolboys again. I recall one evening when all the fire extinguishers were discharged in a mock battle and another when some buttered scones, provided for our late snack, ended up stuck to the lounge ceiling. It was a tall room and there was a competition to see who could throw them forcibly enough to stick there.

3

OIL WORKS

"What do managers do?"
"Easy! They plan, organise, co-ordinate and control."
"Yes but what do they actually do?"
"Well ..."

Norman Venus (sometime ICI training manager)

As I mentioned in Chapter 2, the Billingham factory was built after the First World War by the Brunner Mond company, one of the forerunners of ICI, for the synthesis of ammonia from hydrogen and nitrogen. Most of the ammonia was converted into fertiliser. ICI had always looked for other uses for the hydrogen and this became more urgent when sales fell after the 1929 recession. The answer ICI found was the hydrogenation of coal to petrol and aviation fuel, thus providing an indigenous source of a vital material. It was encouraged by the government, who levied a lower rate of duty on home-produced oils. The Prime Minister, Ramsey MacDonald, opened the Works in 1935. The raw material was powdered coal suspended in creosote. Though part of the Billingham site, the plant was organised as a distinct works under its own works manager, and was known as the Oil Works.

Oil Works moves with the times
At the outbreak of the Second World War the use of coal was discontinued, as it would have been difficult to shut the plant down quickly in

an emergency. Creosote, a by-product of coke production, was used instead. After the war the long-term future of the Works was uncertain. Its profitability depended entirely on a tax advantage, which might be removed at any time, and its contribution to the nation's petrol requirements was negligible. A programme of diversification was therefore begun. ICI modified much of the high-pressure coal hydrogenation equipment for the production other chemicals: plasticiser alcohols, such as nonanol and octanol, butanols, isopropanol (for conversion to acetone) and phenol. The modified plants were started up in 1950 and 1951 and were well established by the time I arrived in January 1952. Petrol production continued on a reduced scale and did not finally stop until 1958. The new plants were very different from the old ones, with modern control rooms and a good deal of automatic control.

Across the River Tees at Wilton ICI had built, after the War, a group of plants — the Olefine Works — for the manufacture of ethylene, propylene and butylene from naphtha. Some of the products were piped under the river to Oil Works. Propylene, for example, was used to make butanols (by reaction with carbon monoxide and hydrogen) and isopropanol (by reaction with water), both at a pressure of 250 bar. Oil Works was thus an exciting place to be; many changes had occurred and old and new plants were operating side by side.

I spent my first few months, partly on days and partly on shifts, training with shift managers, foremen and operators, rather as I had done on the Water Gas Plant six years earlier, but the culture was very different. The operators, on the whole, had much more understanding of the process, and the foremen and chargehands spent most of their time on technical problems rather than on supervising the comparatively few process workers who reported to them. A typical shift foreman had two chargehands and ten process workers under him.

Iso-octane Plant manager

I was scheduled to be a holiday relief shift manager and then a plant manager. The four regular shift managers were former foremen but a young graduate was employed as a fifth man during the summer. It was excellent experience for the graduate but the Works suffered as the young graduates were inexperienced and the practice was dropped a few years later. Fortunately there was also a general foreman on shifts, in the next office, who deputised for the shift manager and he helped the young graduate along.

Soon after I arrived, however, one of the plant managers left the company. Instead of becoming a shift manager I took his place and started on the most enjoyable three years in my career. I would say now, looking back, it was even more enjoyable than my long spell in safety. The plant to which I was appointed, called the US Plant (as the process was licensed from Universal Oil Products of Chicago), made iso-octane, used to boost the octane rating of aviation fuel. It was not closely integrated with the rest of the Works and was located on the other side of a public road, a good 10 minutes' walk from the Works offices. As a result senior managers rarely visited the site and I was left to run my own show, just as I had been left to run the infra-red show during Bill Price's year away.

About the process

The process was a fascinating one as it involved three reaction stages as well as separation and purification steps. In the first stage of the plant

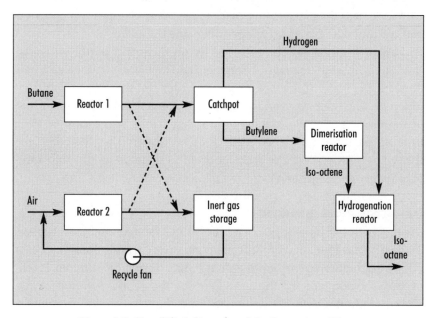

Figure 3.1: Simplified diagram of the Iso-octane Plant

butane, a by-product of petrol production, was dehydrogenated to butylene by passing it through catalyst tubes, heated by hot furnace gas to about 570°C. In the course of the reaction, carbon was deposited on the catalyst and after an hour or so it had to be burnt off. A complex series of automatic valves controlled by a clock (the time cycle controller) diverted the butane to a second parallel reactor, swept out the first reactor with inert gas and then added about 2% oxygen to the inert gas to burn off the carbon (see Figure 3.1). Similar processes are still marketed (Clark R G et al, *Energy Progress*, Vol 7, No 3, September 1987, p164). In the second stage the butylene was dimerised (that is, two molecules were joined together) and then in the third stage the product was hydrogenated to iso-octane.

Built in 1940, the US Plant was the first one in the Works to use automatic controllers, the petrol plants being mainly hand-controlled.

Besides the three reaction stages, the plant included raw material storage and its own cooling water tower and drainage system with oil/water separator. Steam, nitrogen and compressed air were supplied from the main Billingham factory site. The site also housed a small batch unit which used some of the butylene to make an antioxidant.

ICI and chemical engineers

The plant had been operating for 12 years; the shift foremen were experienced and fully capable of dealing with normal operation and with any problems that might arise. Everything that could go wrong had gone wrong before, so the foremen knew exactly what to do and just got on with it, despite the lack of any up-to-date operating instructions (something I was to remedy). The plant was thus an ideal one for a young manager to learn the trade, to learn how plants operate, both technically and administratively, and to learn how their performance can be improved. The apprenticeship I was able to serve for my first 6-12 months was particularly valuable as I was a chemist, not a chemical engineer. I had little knowledge of the factors that affect a dynamic process, or of plant equipment and the way it worked. The little I had picked up was on the Water Gas Plant where things were very different. I had no idea, for example, what a steam trap did or how it worked until a foreman explained it was a device for removing condensed steam from steam lines.

Chemical engineering is a far better training for a plant manager than chemistry but at that time ICI refused to recognise the existence of chemical engineering as a distinct profession. It was prepared to recruit chemical engineers but they had to pretend to be either chemists or engineers. If they chose chemistry, they followed the normal career path for a chemist: research, plant management, perhaps Technical Department. Even the boilers were managed by chemists. If they chose engineering, they followed the engineer's path, alternating between design and plant maintenance. This attitude did not change until the early 1960s when the first chemical engineers became senior enough to influence policy.

ICI's attitude to chemical engineers was very different from that of Du Pont, a company which had many contacts with ICI. Du Pont started a chemical engineering section in 1929 and found that it increased understanding of physical phenomena and made design easier (*Chemical Engineering Progress*, Vol 85, No 9, August 1989, p62).

How the hierarchy worked

Each plant manager had a sort of engineer shadow who maintained the plant. The manager was responsible for production, the engineer for repairs. They had equal status and reported to different bosses and this was reflected throughout the Works organisation (Figure 3.2). In the 1970s we experimented with "manageers" who combined the two jobs but the experiment was not a success as few people had the necessary skills.

I was thus in the middle of the Works hierarchy, which was the normal range of my contacts, but between the works manager and the company chairman there were another six layers, starting with a production manager and above him a production director. Today organisations are slimmer.

The works manager was usually a chemist so the works engineer had much more autonomy than the deputy works manager who could be, in effect, the production or operations manager but was sometimes more of a dogsbody, doing odd jobs for the works manager, as I found out later (see Chapter 5).

In addition to those appearing in Figure 3.2, there were also a number of managers and engineers with Works-wide responsibility: the

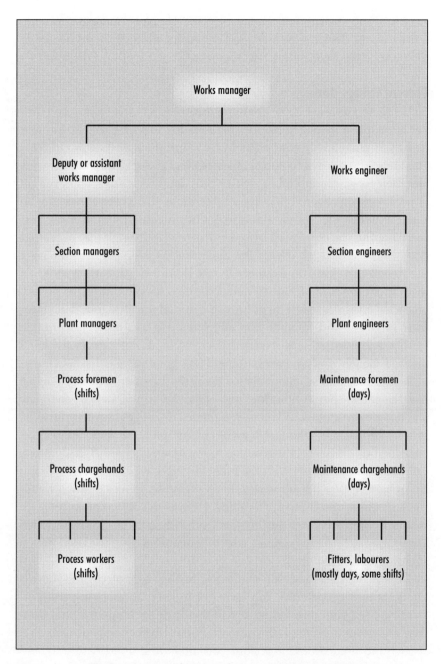

Figure 3.2: Typical ICI works organisation pre-1980

electrical and instrument engineers, the laboratory manager, records officer, works clerk (office manager) etc, each with their own foremen or assistants. The organisation was typical of an ICI works at the time.

Getting things done

Today there are fewer levels but one feature is still the same: the number of people a manager can instruct is much smaller than the number he has to persuade, cajole or lobby. A plant manager has to cultivate good relations with his engineer, the electrical and instrument engineers and their foremen, and other service providers or nothing will ever get done. I soon discovered that in each hierarchy there is one person who is the "gatekeeper", to use a phrase not invented at the time, a key person who must be convinced before you can pass through that particular door. No electrical job except the most routine ever got done unless I convinced the electrical engineer that it should be, but if I wanted an instrument job done I had to persuade the chargehand. If he agreed, obstacles disappeared. If he did not, it counted for little that the instrument engineer and foreman had approved. He was not awkward. He simply knew what was practicable. If I could not convince him, I realised the job was not worth doing. I had great respect for his views.

In the mechanical maintenance team the foreman, Tommy Angus, was the gatekeeper. A fitter foreman of the old school, he was energetic and outspoken, but would move mountains if you got him on your side. When I kept asking when a job would be complete, he said, "Bugger off back to your office and I'll give you a ring when it's ready". In contrast, I did not see eye-to-eye with the plant engineer who had been brought up to believe that his job was to keep maintenance costs down rather than maximise the company's profits. He was the only man in ICI with whom I completely lost my temper and indulged in an uncontrolled slanging match. A chargehand who overheard us congratulated me on standing up to him.

The technique, then, for managing in that sort of organisation is good-natured persistence. You have got to keep on lobbying and persuading until your job is done. It will finally dawn on people that since they are going to have to do your job ultimately, they may as well do it sooner and reduce the hassle, but you must do it good-naturedly and never pull rank. Even when dealing with the people who are responsible to you the situation is little different. If you cannot convince your staff that a certain action is desirable they can find innumerable reasons for delay.

Lines of demarcation were very strict. Process operators could not, of course, use tools and each trade — fitters, electricians, instrument artificers, etc — jealously and zealously guarded the jobs that were traditionally theirs.

Tackling performance

The plant on the whole ran very steadily and I was free to concentrate on improvements. A rise in raw material usage took a lot of tracing. I finally tracked it down to leaking relief valves and set up regular checks. I had small branches fitted to the relief tail pipes of several large relief valves (they all discharged to atmosphere) and once per week they were swept out with nitrogen. Twenty minutes later a sample was taken and analysed for gas. This is a source of loss that many plant managers ignore.

Some years later a colleague found another way of detecting leaking relief valves. He fitted thin plastic tubes, closed at one end, rather like a large sausage skin or condom, to the tail pipes. Normally the plastic drooped. If there was a leak it rose and ultimately burst. It produced some comment at the time.

Plant costs were calculated once per quarter and arrived a month later. They were looked upon as interesting background information rather than a crucial verdict on the plant's operations. Output was watched more closely. This was to change before the end of the decade. By this time salesmen had to sell products instead of allocating them.

Early in my time on the plant I learnt the value of looking at problems numerically, something that was later to play a large part in my career. The day I took over the plant it was shut down for a change of catalyst, a task carried out by the maintenance organisation. The plant engineer reported that several catalyst tubes were choked. He could change them, thus extending the shutdown by two days, or blank them off and change them at the next shutdown in six months' time, when it could be done under cover of other work. What should he do?

I asked the section manager. He was also new to the job, having taken over only a week before, so we both went to see the deputy works manager. (He seemed an awe-inspiring and distant figure, though I was to be sitting in his chair nine years later.) In reply, he said, "Which will lose more output, blanking the tubes or extending the shutdown?" This single remark, more than any other, affected my future outlook. From then on I tried to look at problems numerically. (Of course, at other times the right question would be, "Which would lose the least profit?")

Leaders and leadership

When I went on holiday, I gave the colleague appointed to relieve me some notes on the readings he should watch (reported in the foremen's daily log) and the actions to take if they departed from par. I then realised that many of my so-called managerial decisions were in fact programmed (though I would not have used that word at the time) and that my "Notes on the Foreman's Log" was the program. I gave the foremen a copy too and this encouraged them to take on more responsibility.

I am far from believing that we are mere computers, but nevertheless many of the decisions we make are programmed. We would find it hard to get through the day if every decision required the full exercise of our critical faculties and so, without always recognising the fact, we make them in accordance with a series of programmes or rules of thumb.

My fellow managers were mainly chemists, like myself in their late twenties or thirties, but a few had risen from the ranks through foreman and shift manager. They managed the technically simpler plants but the best of them could hold his own with any graduate. One of my fellow managers at the time, Alan Robertson, later became a member of the main board of ICI but he showed few signs then of the abilities that would take him rapidly to the top. Another future main board director, Philip Harvey, who was with me in Research Department seemed to spend much of his time belly-aching. Spotting high fliers is not easy. In contrast, one of the plant engineers, Bob (later Sir Robert) Malpas, who became managing director of BP and Eurotunnel co-chairman, stood out as someone who would get on — a future works engineer it seemed to us, as that was as far as our horizons stretched. He stood out all the more because most of the engineers were former draughtsmen and there were only a few graduates amongst them.

Despite the rapid expansion of the Works and the introduction of new processes (using mainly old equipment) the attitude of the senior managers to change — generally designed to increase output or improve efficiency — was cautious, to say the least. "Along this tree from root to crown, ideas flow up and vetoes flow down" (graffiti seen on a British Airways noticeboard next to an organisation chart and quoted in their magazine, *Business Life*, No 18, December 1988/January 1989). The most modest capital expenditure (over £50, equivalent to about £1,000 today) required approval by innumerable people and the authorisation forms ran aground in people's intrays. You had to follow them around and cajole people into pushing them off the sandbanks into the stream again. It was sometimes possible — and easier — to persuade a gatekeeper to disguise a change as maintenance. The faint-hearted gave up and ceased trying to improve.

Sir John Harvey-Jones, later chairman of ICI, has described a similar experience when he was a 23-year-old member of the Cabinet Office staff: "Not for a moment had I dreamed that the leadership applied from the top took the form of largely negative interventions on the ideas flowing from below" (*Getting it Together*, Heinemann, London, 1991, p162). At Billingham all this was to change markedly by 1960 when a younger generation took over (see Chapter 5).

The negative attitude of leadership in the 1950s may have been a legacy of the 1914-18 war. So many of the young men of the time were killed that the rest of their generation were promoted above the level that they would otherwise have reached. During a drought they put bricks in toilet cisterns instead of stopping streams of water running to waste.

Labour relations

In ICI each plant manager was responsible for his labour relations. He managed the men as well as the technology, and personnel officers were there to advise. This is a far better system than one in which people are responsible to one manager for "rations and discipline" and to another for technical advice. For the managed there is only one master — for the manager, everything is under his control. Senior people may be able to cope with more than one boss but it is more difficult at other levels.

In 1952 labour relations were much easier than they were to become a decade or so later. The shop stewards were on the whole reasonable men, prepared to listen to you, provided you listened to them. I spent, like most managers, a good part of my time talking to foremen, charge-hands and operators, not just about the job, but in order to get to know them better. It was, of course, one of my jobs to pick out those who were suitable for promotion to chargehand or foreman, to recommend them for promotion outside the plant and to hope someone would do the same for me.

I was surprised how often the foreman and operators vividly recalled the 1930 recession and its effects. In 1952 it seemed a long time ago to me. Now that I am older the events of 20 years ago seem quite recent.

At the time bonus schemes were being introduced throughout the Works and the US Plant had already gone on bonus before I arrived. It was really just a demanning payment but there was an elaborate pretence that it was all based on fair and accurate measurement of the precise work done. Work Study officers measured people with stop-watches. Values were assigned to every task, routine or special, and clerks worked through mountains of paper to calculate the bonus. If you asked a man to move a drum he expected a few "units" but at least was willing to carry out extra jobs in exchange for them (unless it was prohibited by union rules). In ICI you could get away with a lot provided you made it look like part of the current bandwagon.

I made a reduction in manning (from six to five operators per shift). Technically it was easy and my predecessor had started the necessary changes: a few additional instruments so that we did not need someone in the compressor house. Human relations needed more attention. The key was to plan ahead so that no-one was redundant. One or two men were kept on temporarily after normal retirement age; those who left were not replaced and a little overtime was worked or men borrowed from other plants. In the end no-one was without a regular job. And, of course, an increase in bonus had to be arranged. This was easy. All I had to do was invent work, by adjusting the number of readings or plant tours, to give the bonus I thought necessary.

Another important feature was attention to detail. I drew up schedules that showed in detail who would take each reading and carry out each task. When at a meeting the operators started discussing who should read the absorber top pressure, I knew I was home and dry.

What management means

In 1954 my section manager changed. The new manager, Henry Simpson, moved across from one of the other sections and I was warned that he would be difficult to work for. One colleague painted a dismal picture of life under the Simpson jackboot. Nothing could have been further from the truth. Like Bill Price, he was one of the best bosses I ever had.

True, he wanted to know in detail what was happening — and I had a long talk with him on the "phone every morning before 9.00 am. He was far too clued up for anyone to get away with flannel, but as long as I knew what was happening, there was no problem. He delegated well. Despite his wish to know the detail, he did not tell me what to do and I always felt I was in charge. Delegation does not mean withdrawal. A manager who delegates should still observe and be ready to intervene when necessary.

Most managers gathered in the shift manager's office every morning at about 8.45 am, but the Iso-octane Plant was the furthest away and I used this as an excuse for not attending. I went straight to the plant in the morning and stayed there until about 11.00 am, talking to the foreman, chargehand and operators, the plant engineer and his foreman, the instrument chargehand and so on. After a senior member of the Technical Department had visited the plant and pointed out that the sequence of temperatures on a distillation column could not possibly be correct, I made it a habit to look at every reading on the record sheets every day.

From 11.00 am until about 4.30 pm I worked in my office in the Works office block — a series of wooden huts — and then visited the plant again before going home. I would finish by chatting to the foreman until 5.30 or 6.00 pm; the maintenance workers finished at 4.30 pm and the plant became quieter. The foreman made a pot of tea (some made it at 3.00 pm when their shift started and left it to brew on the radiator!) and had more time to chat than in the morning. Ten years later, as assistant works manager, I told new managers that while there was room for variation in management style, if they found they were spending less than three hours per day on the plant, they should ask themselves if it was enough.

Time and the plant manager

Today, as then, many managers say that there is so much paperwork to get through that they cannot spend that long on the plant. Other managers nevertheless manage to do so. Organising their time is a task that many managers find difficult. For some reason paperwork is compelling, though much of it is not very important and, of course, some people find offices warmer and more comfortable than the plant. At this stage of my career I learnt to dictate letters and memos, and this saved a lot of time. I often visited the plant at the weekend, sometimes because there were problems, on other occasions just to show the flag. This was normal. Although there was a roster of duty managers whom the shift manager could ring, they were there as a last resort. He normally tried to ring the plant manager if there were any problems.

On several occasions, when visiting the plant at the weekend, I found instruments badly in need of attention. We had our own shift fitter but there was one shift instrument artificer (known as a tiffy) for the whole Works. The shift manager allocated his time. The foreman had already asked for him but had been told he was not available. I asked the shift manager to call out a day tiffy, saying I would take responsibility. Faced with this evidence of the importance I attached to the instrument faults, the shift manager always made the tiffy available. This was, I think, the nearest I ever came to putting the interests of my patch above those of the company as a whole. Unfortunately many senior managers could not say the same. I could see that if managers were judged on the profits made by their sections, the temptation to increase them at the expense of other parts of the company was great. To quote an Esso manager, "The larger the organisation, the greater the scope for mini-empires, each tending to treat the other units within the organisation as alien bodies" (Fennor H L, *Petroleum Review*, Nov 1984, p9).

Acetone Plant manager

About the end of 1953 the Acetone Plant was added to my responsibilities. Controlled by the same foreman (though with its own chargehand) and located near the Iso-octane Plant, it formed an obvious addition though it was technically not connected. Isopropanol in the form of an azeotrope containing about 14% water, made on the Works main site, was dehydrogenated over a catalyst at low pressure to acetone and hydrogen. The acetone was purified by distillation, and the hydrogen was compressed to 250 bar and sent to the main site. The plant ran very smoothly and gave little trouble. It was the only brand new plant on the

Works, all the other "new projects" being converted from redundant petrol plant equipment, and the control room was one of the Division's show pieces.

ICI put out an advertisement, shown in Figure 3.3, which contrasted the Acetone Plant control room (see photograph between pages 48 and 49) with the method used until the 1950s for controlling the reactors in which nitroglycerine was manufactured. The operators sat on one-legged stools and if they fell asleep they fell off. In later years I made much use of this picture, contrasting it with later nitroglycerine plants which contained far smaller amounts of hazardous material. Instead of

Figure 3.3: Silent Witness — an extract from a 1950s ICI advertisement
The following is part of the text that accompanied the advertisement:
In days gone by, the manufacture of nitroglycerine was controlled by men seated on one-legged stools. It was reckoned that, if the strain of unbroken concentration made them sleepy, they would fall over and wake up. Modern control methods in chemical works present a different picture. The Acetone Plant at ICI's Billingham works, for example, contains nearly a hundred controls, yet is looked after by only two men — constantly on watch to make sure everything is working smoothly. The main factor in bringing about this great change is Instrumentation.

making plants safer by adding on protective equipment that might fail or be neglected, it is far better — if you can — to reduce the amount of material in the plant so that it hardly matters if it all leaks out. I wrote a paper called "What you don't have, can't leak" (see page 100).

With the increased workload I had less time to spend on improving efficency. I soon had to plan a major modification to the Acetone Plant, though it was not complete until after I had left. Sales of polyethylene were expanding rapidly and the Ethylene Plant across the river at Wilton was operating to capacity. A second ethylene plant was not due on stream for several years and more ethylene was needed urgently. It was therefore decided to convert one of the three acetone reactors so that it could be used, with a different catalyst, for the dehydration of ethanol to ethylene. Technical Department handled the project but I was closely involved.

Quirks of organisational training

On the Acetone Plant, as the catalyst aged, the temperature had to be raised to maintained output, but this caused rapid ageing of the catalyst. I told the foremen that the temperature of the product leaving the reactor was not to be raised above 180°C without my authority. Several years later, after I left the plant, my successor telephoned to say that the foremen were very reluctant to let the temperature on the ethylene reactor go above 180°C and did I know why.

Sometimes people take little notice of instructions. Sometimes they carve them on tablets of stone and follow them strictly and unthinkingly, even though the "rules" were designed for different circumstances, in this case for a different catalyst and a different product. Perhaps rules are followed most readily when they fill a vacuum — when there is no other guidance — and least readily when a change in custom and practice is required. In *The Periodic Table* (Michael Joseph, London, 1985, pp147-159), Primo Levi gives another example of a rule followed long after the reason for it had been forgotten. Soon after the War he was working in a paint factory. Some batches of paint set solid and he traced the fault to an impurity in some of the raw material. He cured the problem by adding a small amount of ammonium chloride. Over ten years later he returned to the factory and found that it was still being added although the raw material had long been free from the impurity.

I find it difficult, in this survey of my duties, to convey the interest and enjoyment of the job, but it was one of the most satisfying periods of my career. I had a clearly-defined task and was left in peace to get on with it. There was a continuous series of interesting (though not too difficult) technical problems to solve. If these dried up, there were lots of things I could think of to improve output or efficiency. As well as the technical problems, there was the art of managing. Everything I did was done through other people and they had to be asked, cajoled, persuaded, sweethearted (call it what you will) to co-operate. There were also a few personnel problems — for example, knowing which men did not get on together and should not be put in the same shift team.

Tar Acids Plant manager

At the beginning of 1955 I was transferred to the Refined Tar Acids Plant, which was also under the control of the same section manager, Henry Simpson. The creosote used for the production of petrol contained a few percent of "tar acids" — mainly phenol, cresols and xylenols — which were extracted and separated by batch distillation. I was responsible for the distillation unit and also for two other small stills which purified various alkylated phenols, including *ortho*-phenylphenol (OPP) and *para*-phenylphenol (PPP), by-products of phenol manufacture. I was also responsible for the packing and despatch of the products. Most of the Billingham products were packed by a specialist organisation but the tar acids and related products were handled locally, as there were so many grades of varying purity which had to be carefully matched against customers' requirements.

I cut short my Christmas holiday and returned to work on 1 January 1955 in order to have about ten days' hand-over from my predecessor. I need not have bothered: he took a rather easy-going attitude to the job. Having just returned from holiday himself he did nothing on his first day back, and not much for the rest of the ten days. He is reputed to have left an instruction for his foremen, before going away for a week-end: "If any difficulties are experienced, take appropriate action." It may not be true, but it is significant that it was told about him. I could not stand his style of management but could hardly change anything while he was still around and officially in charge. Finally, on a Friday morning he said "Good-bye" and left me a plant full of trouble: products off-specification, output down and lines choked. Many of the materials handled were solid at ambient temperature and had to be handled in steam-traced lines. The tracing was often faulty or inadequate and chokes were common. If they could not be cleared with a steam lance the lines had to be dismantled.

Dealing with a cultural change

On the Iso-octane and Acetone Plants the foremen and chargehands knew the plants intimately and were able to cope with almost any operating problem. On the Tar Acids Plant they floundered. They seemed unable to diagnose faults and had few rules of thumb to use instead. They did not know all the lines or where they went. For example, there were rows of steam traps associated with the steam tracing but no-one knew which trap served which section of steam tracing, as the connecting lines were all lagged together. On the Iso-octane and Acetone Plants I had left the foremen to run the plant and concentrated on ways of improving performance. In contrast, the new job was a continual battle to maintain output. It was hard to believe I was in the same section of the same works. (It was a characteristic of ICI that quite small units had their own micro-culture so that a move across the road could take you into a different world. A career in ICI provided splendid variety, not only of jobs but of working environment. My impression is that many other large organisations are much more uniform.)

When I left the plant 18 months later I wrote in my hand-over notes:

It has been traditional on the Tar Acids Plant to press on regardless with production although steam leaks are blowing, glands are leaking, instruments are not working and the plant is falling to bits. I have awarded no medals for this heroism as its ultimate result is that far more extensive repairs than were originally necessary have to be made at inconvenient times. For example, if leaking joints in steam lines are ignored the faces of the joints become damaged and new flanges have to be fitted. I have tried to persuade the plant personnel to abandon their old ways and give defective plant to maintenance. I have been favoured in this policy by a shortage of crude tar acids which has made it necessary to shut the stills down from time to time. Nevertheless I am sure the policy is the right one in any case.

Coping with batch processes

The foremen, chargehands and operators on the plant had a reputation in the Works as a bunch of incompetents, always putting materials in the wrong tank, failing to achieve output targets, letting lines choke and so on. This was unfair. They made more errors because on batch plants there are more opportunities for errors. On continuous plants alterations are few and usually gradual. On batch plants conditions, flows, temperatures and so on are being changed all the time; there is never a quiet shift. Before, during and after my stay on the plant some of the best people from the continuous plants were transferred to the batch plants to try to improve standards, but without success.

I had an assistant but he spent his time planning the production schedule, which he did very competently, and was not involved in plant operations, for which he had little aptitude. When he went on holiday and I had to do his job I soon I realised that he was a computer, and that his decisions on which batch to run on which still could all be decided from a few simple rules. He was not a fraud; he simply did not realise that he was programmed. (Artificial intelligence has been defined as "the science of making machines do things that would require intelligence if done by men". It follows, though this is often not recognised, that some tasks that seem to require intelligence may not really do so.)

The production of OPP and PPP had been interrupted a few months before my arrival by a fire, in which a man had unfortunately been killed, and the plant had been extensively modified to avoid similar accidents in the future. I had to start-up the modified unit virtually from scratch. It was a difficult unit to operate as OPP melts at 56°C and PPP at 165°C so the slightest fault in the steam tracing caused everything to set solid. I was proud that my team achieved higher output rates than were ever achieved subsequently.

The start of an interest in safety

During 1955 I was appointed the Works part-time safety officer, a chore carried out by one of the plant managers. Perhaps I was chosen because I took a little more interest in the subject than some of my colleagues. I was expected to spend no more than a few hours a week on this job for which I received no training. I was assisted by an elderly foreman who dealt with such matters as ordering protective clothing, keeping accident statistics, liaison with the Billingham Site Safety Department, attendance at accident investigations (I attended only the more important), perusal of minor accident reports, and so on. He toured the Works looking for obvious mechanical hazards such as tripping hazards and chivvied people to do something about them. The set-up illustrated the attitude to safety at the time. There was concern that people should not get hurt but there was no realisation that the subject required a technical input, or the attention of a senior and experienced manager. In my hand-over notes when I left the job after a year I recall writing that safety was a dull subject apart from the occasional description of a gory accident, a view I was to change later.

Atttitudes to pollution as well as safety were different in those days. If anyone commented on the amount of phenol we put down the drain I said that it was an antiseptic and helped to sweeten the drains. There was some truth in this, as all the sewage from Teesside also went untreated into the River Tees, but it is no longer a sustainable argument.

While managing the Iso-octane Plant I had been involved in one accident that brought my responsibilities for safety home to me. A member of the Research Department wanted to carry out some measurements on a caustic soda line by fitting a contraption made from wires and a rubber bung onto a branch on the line. The foreman and I thought it looked too weak to withstand the pressure but the research worker assured us that it had been used safely before. I agreed to let him go ahead but the foreman and I decided to watch from a safe distance. The contraption leaked and sprayed caustic soda over the pumphouse. Unfortunately it also sprayed a labourer who had entered just before the experiment started and who, like the postman in one of G K Chesterton's Father Brown stories, we had not noticed. The ambulance was called and he was rushed off to the Medical Centre and washed down. An hour later he returned to his job, seemingly none the worse, but later developed an allergic reaction and was off work for a few days. Henry Simpson wrote the report on the incident and attached all the blame on the research worker who, he said, should have known what pressure his equipment would withstand. Nevertheless as the manager responsible for everything on the plant I felt morally responsible. I realised I should have asked the researcher what pressure his contraption could withstand and if it had been tested at that or a higher pressure.

Transfer

In mid-1956, after 18 months on the Tar Acids Plant, I was transferred to the Technical Department. I was glad of the move. The work on the plant had been physically exhausting and I was ready for a move to a job that was not a continual battle against recalcitrant equipment. It was the hardest 18 months of my career. Also I had now reached the maximum salary for a plant manager and had no rise in salary the previous Christmas. Further advancement depended on promotion in the Works, of which there seemed no prospect, or a move to another Department.

As a parting present the plant won (jointly with another plant) the Billingham Site plant tidiness award. As the plant, when I arrived, had been unbelievably filthy, I felt this was quite an achievement for all concerned. On the Acetone Plant, anything that was spilt evaporated. On the Refined Tar Acids Plant it set solid and had to be removed with pick and shovel or worse still, turned to tar, and was trampled all over the place. People had come to accept the filth as inevitable and had to be persuaded that they could do something about it. I think the effort was worthwhile because if a plant is untidy, people easily (though not inevitably) become sloppy in their methods of work. It is easier to run a "tight ship" if it is tight in every respect. I used to spend a couple of hours every Monday morning going round the plant with the process foreman on duty and the maintenance foreman, drawing their attention to any muck that we could find. The better foremen soon got the message and carried out their own inspections the day before.

Considerable importance was attached to plant tidiness in the mid-1950s and every site held competitions and inspections. Fashions changed in the 1970s and standards slipped. In later years it has been my good fortune to visit plants in many countries and I found few as untidy as those at Billingham and Wilton became in the 1970s.

4

TECHNICAL DEPARTMENT

*James will tell you what to do and what answer he expects
you will get, and then leave you to get on with it.*

Remark made by a colleague when I joined Technical
Department

Billingham Division Technical Department in 1955 consisted of
about six senior managers of works manager status, each assisted by between four and six chemists. Some of the chemists were
passing through; others were fixtures. All had research and production
experience, though in some cases rather a long time ago. The department had two functions that would be separated in most organisations
today.

The first function was to decide — or more precisely to recommend
to the appropriate management committee and the Division Board —
when new production capacity was required, how much extra capacity
was needed, and which manufacturing process should be used. This
involved close liaison with the appropriate works, the Marketing,
Research, Engineering and Accountancy Departments and contractors.
It was to a large extent a co-ordinating role but the staff played a key
role in choice of process and did most of the detailed work necessary for
the preparation of expenditure proposals.

The second function was the design of the flowsheet which was then passed on to the Engineering Department for costing and, if sanctioned, for engineering design. Although Engineering Department had to prepare "sanction quality" costs, we made our own quick calculations to help us decide which options were feasible. The process design was really a job for chemical engineers but there were few of them about and chemists had to, and did, get by.

Designing for *para*-xylene

Each of the sections of the Department was concerned with a different range of products and I was allocated to the Petroleum Chemicals Section, headed by James Woolcock. It had been responsible for the design of the plants at Wilton that produced ethylene, propylene and butylene by cracking naphtha, some of the downstream plants which used their products and other plants included in the Olefine Works at Wilton. My particular responsibility was the production of *para*-xylene made by isomerisation of mixed xylenes followed by crystallisation of the *para*-xylene and its extraction by centrifuging.

In my two years in the Department I designed an extension and several modifications and saw them commissioned, but the new plant (No 3) that I designed was never built. It was similar to Nos 1 and 2 (which were carbon copies). When a new plant was finally built in the early 1960s many changes were made to the design and it was called No 4. I also did a number of odd jobs from time to time, usually quick assessments of the feasibility of various ideas that the Department was asked to look into.

The move to Technical Department was a big change. Instead of being on the margins, responsible for the production of by-products of the Division's main activities, I was at the heart of things. I had to learn how profitability was estimated, how plants were costed and how plate-by-plate calculations on distillation columns and a number of other chemical engineering calculations were carried out, all matters that are covered in chemical engineering courses but not in the training of chemists. I had frequent contact with senior members of the Division. One of the managing directors, Douglas Bell, took a particular interest in our work; his office was only a few doors away and he was always looking in. There were meetings with staff from other Divisions and organisations and, though I was often only the dogsbody who took the notes, it gave me an insight into events as well as a series of good lunches.

Early computing

I used a computer for several iterative calculations — a mass balance and plate-by-plate distillation calculations. The latter were carried out in collaboration with an outstanding mathematician, Frank Roesler. Unlike the other mathematicians I worked with, he was not willing simply to program my formulae but made sure he understood the physical reality behind them. The computer we used was an Elliott valve-operated model with less computing power than a first generation PC, but it seemed wonderful at the time. To estimate the number of plates required in a distillation column it had to be left on overnight, repeatedly calculating compositions up and down the column.

Roesler realised that if we did not understand the reality behind a formula we might use it outside its range of application. The increased use of computers has made this kind of thing more prevalent but you don't need a computer or even a pocket calculator to make this sort of error, as shown by the following simple example from my book *Dispelling Chemical Engineering Myths* (3rd edition, Taylor and Francis, Philadelphia and London, 1996).

During the design of a new plant (costing about £10M) it was decided to strengthen the control building so that it could withstand a vapour cloud explosion. The building designer said that the extra cost would be £30,000 and this was accepted as reasonable. When the project was complete the project manager reported that the strengthening the building had cost an extra £100,000 and an explanation was needed. The project manager had multiplied the £30,000 by a factor of 3.3 to arrive at an overall cost increase of £100,000.

A well-recognised method of estimating plant costs is to multiply the cost of the main plant items (reactors, distillation columns, heat exchangers, etc) by a factor, usually in the range of 3 to 6, depending on the type of plant, to allow for land, foundations, structures, piping, electrical equipment, instruments, ancillary buildings, and utilities as well as design and construction. A factor of 3.3 was the achieved figure for that particular plant. The project manager had treated the control building as a main plant item and multiplied its cost (£30,000) by 3.3.

However, increasing the strength of the control room would have added a little to design and construction costs but would not have increased the costs of land, foundations, structures, piping, electrical equipment, instruments, ancillary buildings, and utilities. The figure of £100,000 had been obtained by using a formula mechanically without thinking of the reality behind it or considering whether it applied in this case.

Contacts with Olefine Works

Most interesting of all my contacts at this time were those with Olefine Works and its staff. As I mentioned in Chapter 3, it was a new works on a new site — across the River Tees at Wilton (see Figure 4.1), on a site acquired in 1946 — and had been started up in 1951. Although part of Billingham Division and a "brother" of Oil Works, the new works had a remarkably different culture, a tribute to the personality of its first works manager, Charles Cockram, and his senior colleagues.

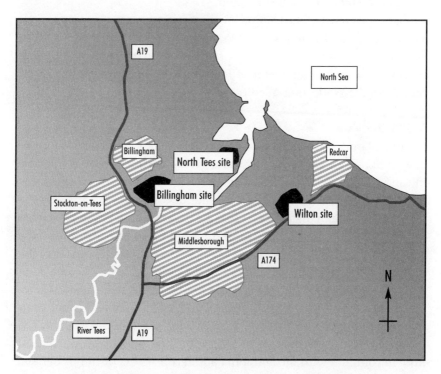

Figure 4.1: The three ICI sites on Teesside — 1980s layout

Because it was a brand new works many of the best people in the Division had been sent there, and it started off with standards of excellence that successive works managers tried hard to maintain. Its staff had better promotion records than those from any other works. Compared with Oil Works the management style was more authoritarian and there was a less tolerant, less easy-going attitude to the less able and the less industrious — at all levels. Unfortunately, the staff had a somewhat arrogant attitude to the rest of the Division which made them very inflexible in meetings. They thought of themselves as the Guards Brigade of the Division and they did not really like having to deal with the Pioneer Corps. Manners required that they listen to what was said but they did not take much notice: it was not by chance their visitors' car park was far too small. I felt I had to work hard to learn the plant and its problems before they would accept me. With my Oil Works background I was rather like a woman in industry at the time. I had to be that little bit better to be accepted.

Of course, most of the Olefine Works staff were decent people as well as competent and barriers were soon down. When the Works culture reinforced a personality that was already arrogant and all-knowing, however, the result could be insufferable. A few such people advanced rapidly in the Works but failed to do so well outside it.

A new Division

My boss, James Woolcock, was an excellent man to work for. He knew how to encourage and advise without giving the impression of interfering and I always felt I was in control of my job. He had one trait that was at first disconcerting. He would ask me to undertake what seemed a mammoth task and then suggest that we discussed my findings the next morning. Did he expect me to work through the night? My office-mate explained that this was his way of saying, "It's not worth spending a lot of time on the problem, just the rest of the day."

On 1 January 1958 Oil Works and Olefine Works were hived off (we would now say demerged) from Billingham (later Agricultural) Division to form a new Heavy Organic Chemicals (HOC) Division. The move was logical as the two works, with their organic products, had little in common with the ammonia and fertilisers made at Billingham. Rapid growth of the organic sector was foreseen and the organisation needed to be ready for it. The demerger set off a spate of promotions. Every department and function was split and new heads of departments and sections had to be appointed. In the Engineering Department, for example, all the senior positions were duplicated. In the main the new opportunities went to the new Division and the existing incumbents stayed with Billingham Division. James Woolcock was appointed Technical Director of HOC Division with a Technical Manager under him (there were a lot of one-over-one appointments).

Twenty years later the two engineering departments were recombined under the name North-East Region Engineering Department. This was abbreviated to NERED and then expanded to Nearly Everyone Redundant Except Directors.

The two Divisions had to share one headquarters building and huts sprang up all around. We were moved into one of these. Fortunately a new office building was already being built so Billingham were able to take that and leave the old building to the new Division.

Divisional cultures

ICI Divisions had remarkably different cultures and strong identities dating back to those of the founder companies that created ICI in 1926. The main board of the company functioned as a holding company, controlling finance and personnel policy but allowing the individual Divisions considerable autonomy.

To some extent the different cultures reflected different problems but there was also a strong element of the sort of nationalism shown by newly independent countries: a desire to maintain and even accentuate differences for their own sake. A new Division, like a new African state, sought to create a new culture and HOC staff liked to think of themselves as more energetic and go-ahead than the fuddy-duddies of Billingham. On the production front, as I was to find when I returned to Oil Works, the "Olefine spirit" was strong and this caused some tensions in Oil Works.

A story went round that the cars belonging to two managing directors, one Billingham, one HOC, came unexpectedly into contact and that remarks were exchanged about there being too many Divisions at Billingham. I do not know if the story was true, but it exemplified the attitudes of the time.

During 1957 a modification to the Acetone Plant had to be commissioned. Start-up proved difficult and the works manager told Technical Department that the plant was inoperable, and if they thought it would work they could come and work it. The chemist who had designed the modification had not worked on a plant for many years so, as a former plant manager, I was sent back to the Works to see if I could sort out the problem. After a few days I managed to puzzle out what was wrong: the control systems on two distillation columns had been designed without reference to each other and there was an unforeseen interaction (coupling) between them. The plant manager was almost there and would have solved it himself had he been left alone a little bit longer.

A serious fire

About the same time there was a serious accident on Oil Works which I used later to illustrate many of the principles of technical safety. When the new projects were constructed in about 1950 some injectors — large high pressure (250 bar) reciprocating pumps, which had previously been used to pump liquids similar to petrol — were used to pump propylene. (It was then converted into butanols, by reaction with carbon monoxide and hydrogen, or into isopropanol, by reaction with water, on the old "petrol plant" reactors.) The injectors were in a building. The studs holding a gland follower in position failed and a massive leak of propylene occurred. It came out of the large open door of the building and was ignited by a furnace 75m away. Four men (including the shift manager and general foreman) had arrived at the scene, and one of them was putting on breathing apparatus in order to enter the building to isolate the leaking injector, when ignition occurred. The four men were badly burnt about the face and hands. I knew two of them well and visited them in hospital and will never forget their black, unrecognisable faces. This provided some of the emotional drive behind my later interest in safety.

The underlying cause of the fire, though we did not see this at the time, was a failure by the plant designers to understand the differences between petrol and propylene. Vapour from a leak of petrol will not spread very far. As a rough rule of thumb, if a spillage is x metres diameter the vapour will be flammable for a further x metres downwind, but vapour from a spillage of liquid propylene can spread for hundreds of metres. The fire was a good example of the unforeseen effects of technical change.

Avoiding another fire

Following the fire, and a long drawn out debate in the management committees concerned, major changes were made to the plant:

- the injectors were resited in the open air, surrounded by a steam curtain to confine and disperse small leaks. They were also fitted with remotely-operated suction, delivery and blowdown valves. If another leak occurred, the injectors could be isolated and blown down from a safe distance.
- a flare stack was provided for the safe disposal of the propylene in the machines when they had to be emptied for repair. Previously, it had simply been spilt on the ground.
- gas detectors gave early warning of leaks.
- the propylene storage vessels were resited well away from operating plant.

Later, after my return to Oil Works, I was to be responsible for commissioning this new equipment. The new design was well thought out and I was later to advocate greater use of the ideas involved but, as we shall see in Chapter 6, the lessons learnt were not passed on to the rest of the company.

Like everyone else in the new Division, I hoped to get some promotion out of the change. The move to Technical Department had been only a small step-up; I was now 35 and so many new section managers had been appointed that I was beginning to feel like the girl who was "always a bridesmaid, never the blushing bride". In the middle of 1958 my turn came and I was transferred back to Oil Works to start a Process Investigation Section.

5

OIL WORKS REVISITED

Throughout the evolution of the chemical industry, safety has been treated as an afterthought. It is the tag-along in a group of kids on the playground: at times annoying yet unavoidable.

Lucas Osborne, *Process Safety Progress*, 18(4):W5, Winter 1999
(Chemical engineering students were invited to write an essay on a safety topic. The quotation is from the winning essay.)

The technical managing director of HOC Division, "Nylon" Palmer, had, when he was Nylon Works manager at Billingham, set up a Process Investigation (PI) Section to look into those technical problems which plant managers did not have time to investigate but which for one reason or another Research and Technical Departments could not or did not wish to look into. Often these problems seemed too trivial to the other Departments; sometimes they were so closely linked to works operations that they could hardly be investigated satisfactorily from outside. Palmer urged the two works managers of the new Division to set up similar sections and I was sent back to Oil Works to start the section there.

Process problems investigated
The fashion at this time and for the following decade was to solve problems by putting more people to work on them. (Later the fashion

changed and problems were solved by getting rid of people.) Many chemists (and chemical engineers pretending to be chemists, but the opposition to chemical engineers was weakening) were transferred to the Works, some from Research Department, some new recruits with previous experience. In general, they were appointed to be plant managers and the managers displaced were transferred to my section to work on the technical problems of their old plants. I also had one or two newcomers in the section from time to time. My staff were thus mainly senior and experienced managers who were in demand elsewhere, so turnover was rapid and membership of the section varied from about four to as many as eight. The members included John Cullen, later, as Sir John, Chairman of the Health and Safety Commission and already standing out as a very competent young man.

I received little or no guidance on the problems we should tackle or how I should tackle them, other than an occasional "Why don't you look at this". Looking back, I can see that we dissipated our energies on too many relatively trivial problems. In contrast, at Olefine Works, where the senior section manager was put in charge of the PI Section, he concentrated most of the section's effort on one major problem, optimisation of the performance of the plants by computer control.

On the whole I found my 18 months in charge of the PI Section less than fully satisfying. I was not entirely sure what I should be doing or if I was doing it. The production manager, Harry North, who came between the production director and the two works managers (a top heavy organisation if ever there was one), took a good deal of interest in our work but his comments were restricted to specific points and none of my immediate bosses took an overview. However, I received a very appreciative note from "Nylon" Palmer when I issued a report on our first year's work. I can still recall the rather peculiar opening sentence: "This I like; not unnaturally it is music to my ears."

Open door policy

After a year in the job, about the middle of 1959, I was transferred back to Technical Department for a couple of months as the man who had taken my place there was on sick leave and no-one else knew anything about the job. When I returned to the Works, the deputy works manager had been replaced by Ron Thomson, a young man from Olefine

Works, still in his early thirties. (The job was now called assistant works manager.) He had been brought in by the Board, and particularly the production director, in order to liven up and "olefinise" what they considered to be the less efficient of the Division's two works. He was without doubt very able, capable of seeing the essentials of a problem very quickly and always knew the right time to interfere, but a moody and abrasive personality prevented him getting as far as he would otherwise have got.

He introduced to the Works a practice I followed for the rest of my career. He disconnected the automatic door closing mechanism on his door and left it open. This encouraged others to drop in and thus improved communication between the staff. If the door was closed it indicated he had someone with him. There may be some jobs in which it is necessary for people to guard themselves against interruption by making visitors go through a secretary's office but the practice is grossly overused, perhaps because it helps people to feel important. On the whole organisations will benefit if office doors are left open and people answer the phone themselves.

In a similar way I learned from James Woolcock not to sit behind my desk if I held a meeting in my office as it distanced me from the others. It was better to sit with them round a table.

Conversion Section

I told Ron Thomson that, despite the interest of the PI job, it did not give the same satisfaction as plant operation and that I hoped for a move to one of the operating sections. At the end of 1959, after 18 months on PI work, I swopped jobs with another section manager and became Conversion Section manager.

Oil Works was organised into three production sections, the By-products Section, in which I had previously worked as a plant manager, the Conversion Section, in which various high pressure reactions were carried out, and the Refinery Section where the products of these reactions were purified by distillation. The products were butanols and higher alcohols made by carbonylation (the reaction of olefins with carbon monoxide), phenol and isopropanol. Petrol production had ceased in 1958. It would have been more logical to have divided the main site (Conversion and Refinery) by product rather than by unit operations

A pencil sketch of me in 1946,
aged 23 and on holiday in Norway,
by "Joan"

My maternal grandfather in Warsaw,
about 1868

Bill Price (as umpire
at a King's College
London cricket
match), 1960s

Bob Malpas,
1960s

John Cullen,
about 1960

Oil Works Council, 1955. L to r, back row, standing: labour department representative, Charles Cowie (plant manager and later ICI company safety adviser), Harry Coath (shop steward and future senior shop steward, see page 54), Laurie Brown (process foreman, injured in 1957 fire), instrument foreman, me (Tar Acids Plant manager), Tom Frankland (Works clerk and office manager), Norman Fuller (senior shop steward); front row, seated: laboratory shop steward, shop steward, Geoffrey Gowing (Works manager), Ernie Bravin (shop steward), shop steward

John Harvey-Jones in 1971, chairman of Petrochemicals Division

US Plant, 1952 — my first plant on Oil Works: the polymerisation reactors

*Replacement plant built after the 1957 Oil Works fire (see page 44)
and which we commissioned in 1960 (see page 49)*

*Acetone Plant Control Room, 1952:
at the time the most modern control room in Billingham Division (see page 31)*

Acetone Plant distillation columns, 1950s

Oil Works tank fire, 1966: see page 66

Tar Acids Plant, 1958: the control room

Conversion Section, 1960: the top of a high
pressure (250 bar) vessel...

...and the spanners for use on it — they
were tightened by hammering

James Woolcock,
early 1950s

Henry Simpson,
1960s

Kenneth Gee,
about 1970

Rab Telfer (l) with Sir Derek Ezra,
chairman of the National Coal Board, 1978

but the Conversion/Refinery split was easy geographically, traditional and the only practical one from a maintenance point of view. The disadvantage was that the Conversion and Refinery Section managers had to spend a lot of time liaising with each other on details and this could and did degenerate into bickering, the two section managers blaming each other for output and quality problems.

I was glad of the move, partly because I was back on production and partly because it was a Billingham site belief that experience on high pressure plants was necessary for promotion, a sign of virility; you were not really a man until you had worked on them. I should not have worried. The need for high pressure experience was Billingham doctrine. The New Testament required Olefine Works experience and I never got that.

During this period we had to commission the new propylene handling equipment already described in Chapter 4. There were many problems. They came all at once and the plant manager began to feel the strain. Finally, I sent him home to get some sleep and put someone else in charge. The new man picked up the detail of the new plant with incredible speed, and soon sorted things out. I remember him coming into the control room and finding the foreman and operators poring over a line diagram looking for possible sites of a choke that was apparently preventing flow. He went straight out to the plant and found a valve shut.

Sometimes a manager has to take action that may upset someone though in this case the man concerned was relieved, not offended. I probably made the change a day later than I should have done but I have always hesitated before taking decisions that may upset people. At least I took it.

A change in attitudes

During 1960 the works manager retired and was replaced by the Olefine Works manager, Kenneth Gee. After a few months he was moved to a job in London and was replaced by another young man from Olefine Works, Edward Challis. At the same time Ron Thomson returned to Olefine Works and Bert Booker from Olefine Works was appointed assistant works manager in his place. A little earlier Mike Boycott had arrived as works engineer so the top hierarchy were all new.

Edward Challis was, like Bill Price and Henry Simpson, one of the handful of really exceptional men that it has been my good fortune to work with. Energetic and technically very able, he could persuade anyone to do anything. He could send you away enthusiastic to carry out what would normally be a tiresome chore. He was the first chemical engineer in the Division to reach works manager status and was able to get chemical engineers recognised as a distinct profession.

Robin Edgeworth Johnstone, professor of chemical engineering at Nottingham at the time, later commented on the change (*The Chemical Engineer*, No 432, January 1987, p338):

> To sum up, the long twilight before chemical engineering was fully recognized in this country appears to have been largely due to the opposition of vested interests within the industrial technocracy. Chemists and mechanical engineers in the big firms had a cosy arrangement to share between them tasks which were beginning to call for something more than a mixture of their two long-standing disciplines.

Earlier in the same article he wrote that in 1964 senior members of a "major British chemical producer" (presumably ICI) donned sackcloth and ashes and said, "We have been wrong".

Under the new management there was a greater willingness to accept change. In 1956 if you had an idea you had to work hard to get it approved and implemented. Now, in 1960, if you had an idea, Edward Challis or Bert Booker was round the next week to ask what you had done about it. What was the reason for delay? For goodness sake, get moving! It was a far more stimulating atmosphere to work in.

Increased responsibilities

Having never worked in Conversion Section as a plant manager I had a lot to learn. I had just reached the stage where I could come in on a Saturday morning and make intelligent comments when my empire was doubled. Edward Challis solved the age-old problem of liaison between Refinery and Conversion Sections by putting them under the same section manager! I was given two senior plant managers — a new grade intermediate between plant manager and section manager — to assist me. I put one in charge of all matters concerning carbonylation — that is, both reaction and purification — and the other in charge of storage, packing and despatch (now taken over by Oil Works). The managers of the isopropanol and phenol plants remained directly responsible to me.

The Phenol Plant was a dreadful one, an assemblage of junk surplus from other projects. When some years later I read Darwin's opinion of orchids (Gould S J, *Ever Since Darwin*, Norton, New York, 1973, p91), "the structures evolved to secure fertilisation by insects are jerry-built of available parts used by ancestors for other purposes", I thought at once of the Phenol Plant.

It was another very busy period and I had to be quite ruthless in cutting out inessential work. We all like to follow up our hobby horses but there was no time for that. It was good experience. Everyone should have a period when they are grossly overworked and thus learn what is essential and what is not. (Unfortunately some people do not learn. I have seen overworked people fiddling with paper of marginal value and not getting out on the plant.) But if periods of overwork go on too long, commoner today with reduced manning, they leave no time for thinking about the wider issues, such as "Are we doing the right thing in the right way?"

The start of the North Tees site

At this time substantial expansion was foreseen and the Division started to develop a new site about six miles from Billingham on land reclaimed from the Tees estuary (see Figure 4.1, page 41). It was known as the North Tees site. On it a small refinery was built, originally half-owned by Shell but later by Phillips, and two aromatics plants. These were to come later. Initially the site was used only for the storage of naphtha which arrived by ship and was pumped to Agricultural Division at Billingham for the manufacture of ammonia. The old process described in Chapter 2 had by now been replaced and ammonia was made from naphtha rather than coke. Oil Works were responsible for the site, though later it became an independent works. I recall being present when the first oil was pumped into the first tank as an incident that occurred was typical of the attitude to technical safety problems at the time.

The tanks were of the floating roof type in which the roof floats on top of the oil and there is normally no vapour space in which an explosive mixture of oil vapour and air can form. However, when the tank is empty the roof rests on supports about 4 feet tall and a vapour space forms below it. When an empty tank is being filled, a mixture of oil vapour and air forms in this space. If ignited it could blow the tank up. It is therefore accepted practice to fill the tank slowly, until the roof is on float, so that the oil does not become charged with static electricity. If it did a spark could pass between the oil and the tank roof or walls and ignite the vapour/air mixture.

We had no means of measuring the flow rate of the oil, so all we could do was ask the ship's officer to pump slowly. He did not, and the roof came on float very quickly, fortunately without trouble.

Today, questions would be asked during design such as "What is a safe flow rate?" "Could there be more flow?" "What will happen if there is more flow?" "How will we know if there is more flow?" "If more flow is hazardous, how can we prevent it?" and so on. They would probably be asked by the designers but they would certainly be asked during a formal study of the design known as a hazard and operability study or Hazop. Not only flow but the possible cause and results of deviations in temperature and pressure and any other important parameters are questioned by applying guide words such as none, more and less. The origin of this technique which emerged formally a few years later is described on page 58.

The Wilton site

Also about this time there was a major change in the organisation of the Wilton site. The site had been started after the war as a sort of trading estate on which various ICI Divisions built and operated plants, while a site organisation provided piped services such as steam, water and compressed air and administrative services such as security, fire-fighting, canteens and medical. About 1961 the site organisation was made part of Heavy Organic Chemicals Division.

The eight or so works managers at Wilton had divided responsibilities. They were responsible to their Divisions for costs and output (and their own career progression) but had to conform to site policy on personnel and other site matters. This was not an easy organisation to administer, especially as the shop stewards were better than the management at cross-site communication and could play one works against another: for example, getting a concession on one works where it hardly mattered and then claiming it across the site.

Joe Roeber has described the situation in his study of ICI labour relations (*Social Change at Work — The ICI Weekly Staff Agreement*, Duckworth, London, 1975, p122):

> ... there was no individual with an interest in running the site as a unit, nor with the power and authority. On the contrary, there was a confusing and conflicting web of responsibility and power in which none of the inter-related systems matched ... The only body with a structure appropriate for operation on a site-wide basis, and the power and the will to do so, was the unofficial committee of senior shop stewards.

Several of the best managers in the company grappled with the Wilton site problem, with less than complete success, and the organisational problem was not finally solved until after I retired, when almost the whole of the Wilton site was organised as a single, large works. Today, as readers will no doubt be aware, it is owned by half a dozen different companies.

Promotion

In May 1961 Bert Booker returned to Olefine Works and, after less than a year in charge of the combined sections, I was, to my surprise, appointed assistant works manager. It was the second big promotion of my career, only three years after the first one. In the six years from 1956 to 1961 I had done six jobs. My colleagues were relieved to see that someone without Olefine Works experience could get promotion above section level.

The 1960s were a time of rapid growth and rapid promotion at all levels, especially of younger people. If I went into a control room and did not know who was in charge, my rule of thumb was to assume that the youngest man was the supervisor.

The next two years were happy and satisfying ones, working closely with Edward Challis. We complemented each other. His approach to the management of Oil Works was, as he admitted, to "kick it where it bulges"; management by exception if you prefer a more high-sounding phrase. He did not have the patience for regularly checking up on things, routinely surveying the scene, and this was left to me. He regarded me as the production manager, paralleling the works engineer.

Edward did take more interest in production than maintenance but nevertheless left me with the feeling that I was running the job.

Labour relations

My worst problems during this period were concerned with labour relations, partly because they had deteriorated in the company as a whole and partly because the senior general worker shop steward on Oil Works, Harry Coath, had an entirely different approach from that of his predecessors. He was confrontative and aggressive rather than conciliatory, preferring conflict to compromise. I had grown up in the very different atmosphere of the early 1950s and was not prepared for the change. I tried to play the game by the old rules, and only slowly — too slowly — came to realise that the rules had changed. A different, tougher approach was needed. Concessions no longer produced peace, but a demand for bigger concessions.

We had a series of formal meetings with the local officials of the trade union, with representatives of the Labour Department in the chair. These "local conferences", as they were called, were previously almost unknown. The shop stewards and management had prided themselves on settling everything at plant or Works level. However, these local conferences always went very well from my point of view as the union officials played the game according to the old rules. They were predictable and if you could find out what was worrying them you could often meet their worries without compromising your own position. For example, as the result of a plant closure some men had to be transferred to a lower-rated job.

To soften the blow and weaken their objections, I said I would "forget" to put through a change of rate form until a few months had passed. Paying a few men a few pence an hour more for a few months was a small price for peace, provided it could not be quoted as a precedent. In ICI we could do that sort of thing.

Getting things done

Another change since the 1950s was that it was much more difficult to get people to do things. As a plant manager six to ten years earlier, if I saw some junk lying around and asked for it to be picked up, it was picked up. Now nothing seemed to happen. In part, this was because I was now more remote from the people who did the picking up, and the message got lost in transit down the line, but there was also a real deterioration in people's willingness to do what they were asked to do, especially if it could be construed as not part of the job. Chris Hampson, a director of ICI somewhat later, once said that in the company, "Sometimes you feel the wheel is not connected to the rudder".

As a plant manager I knew from my daily visits to the plant if my requests had been carried out and if they were successful. Now, at a higher level, I had to make a positive effort to check. The same point is made in the report on the 1988 Clapham Junction railway accident (Hidden H, *Investigation into the Clapham Junction Railway Accident*, Her Majesty's Stationery Office, London, 1989, p158):

> Mr X's skills lay in identifying problems... He was as completely correct in identifying the problem as he was in arriving at correct initial solutions... The difficulty was that that having identified the problem and arrived at solutions, he then turned his attention to other things and made the dangerous assumption that the solution would work and that the problem would go away. In fact it did not.

During the next ten years labour relations deteriorated further. We were to see a few strikes by process operators, something that would have been unthinkable in the 1950s and before, while short strikes and overtime bans by maintenance workers became a regular occurrence. Nevertheless, labour relations, though not as good as in the past, were still far better than in many other companies. Thus Harry Coath, who was a fitter's mate, agreed that I could photograph him doing a job that only a qualified craftsman should have done. There was an unspoken understanding between us that I would never dream of using the photograph to embarrass him. (I wanted it to illustrate an accident and it was cropped before use.)

On another occasion there was a short strike by the process operators on North Tees Works and managers operated the plant. Before they went on strike the operators cleaned up the mess room and left flowers on the tables. Finally, before leaving they kept saying to the managers who were relieving them, "Are you sure you know what to do?" They acted as if the strike was an Act of God that could not be prevented and which everyone had to cope with as well as they could. And they were right. The union acted as a god: remote, arbitrary, authoritative and vengeful.

ICI's policy was to discourage individuals who wanted to work during a strike. It causes bad feeling afterwards and any such "loyal" workers, loyal to company rather than union, were advised to join the strike.

Costs and overheads

In spite of these "labour pains", the period 1961-1963 was a busy and satisfying one, though looking back on these two years I may have interfered too much in the detail. I had been in the Works long enough to know a lot of the detail, sometimes more than the plant and section managers, and understandably they did not like me producing this knowledge when we were discussing problems.

One responsibility of the assistant works manager was the monitoring of the Works costs. Simple costs were now prepared monthly and full costs quarterly. There was always a busy week following the publication of the latter, as I analysed them in detail and prepared comments for the production director. The work was greatly eased when a new chief accountant introduced standard costing. It was now possible to see at a glance how much of a change in cost was due to different raw material usage, fuel usage, change in raw material price, higher maintenance cost and so on. Days of calculations were saved and each part of a change in cost could be laid at the door of the manager or department responsible.

I had to keep a close eye on overheads and was under considerable pressure to reduce them. I was able to do so but only some of the reduction was real. Instead of charging the cost of running the records office or heating the office block, for example, to overheads, they were divided up amongst the products, where their contribution was so small that they went unnoticed. Or Agricultural Division, who operated the Billingham site, were persuaded that they charged us too much for the usage of roads that Oil Works staff rarely used. The overheads appeared to come down and the Board did not ask too many questions.

This fiddling is OK provided someone continues to look at the total cost of running the records office, heating the office block and so on, and of course we did.

Laundering the numbers

As well as pressure on overheads there was pressure on numbers. The figures reported to the Board were not the average number of employees throughout the year but the number on 31 December. I made them look better by telling the labour clerk that any new employees engaged in December should not start work until January. In large companies no-one minds a little laundering of the figures to make them look better, as your boss has to report them to his boss, provided they believe you are really trying to improve the performance.

Of course, the pressure on numbers was not nearly as great as it was to become in later years and so far as technical people were concerned it was the other way. If a works or department had problems, and we often did, then obviously they needed more people to solve them and more were recruited or drafted in from elsewhere. We did not have to ask for them. They were thrust upon us and portacabins grew on the grass around our new office block. As already mentioned, in the 1970s the fashion changed and problems were "solved" by getting rid of people.

One feature which I introduced into the Works at this time — it continued for very many years after I left — was a monthly meeting of all the technical staff. The first half-hour was taken up by a discussion of the costs for the previous month — trends and the reasons for them and actions planned or in hand — and then a visiting speaker gave a short talk. The meeting kept people aware of all that was going on.

Improving technical knowledge

Another innovation tried during this period was the introduction of technical people onto the shift teams in place of foremen. It was not my idea but I picked it up and ran with it. There was a growing feeling that many of the foremen, excellent men though they were in many ways, did not have the technical knowledge and understanding necessary for the supervision of the more complex plants.

We recruited a number of young men with pass degrees or equivalent and put them on shifts in place of the foremen on the By-Products Section. They were expected to take over the technical supervision, but leave the man-management to the assistant foremen who were responsible to them. The experiment was not a success and was quietly dropped after a few years. Nylon Works, however, tried the same experiment and made it work.

More successful, on Oil Works, were our attempts to improve the training of process workers. We encouraged them to attend a local technical college in their free time — the timetable was arranged so that shift workers could attend — and if they passed the City and Guilds ordinary level examination in chemical plant operation we gave them time off to work for the advanced level course. Many of the younger men took advantage of those opportunities. They got no extra pay if they passed — ICI policy, agreed with the trades unions, was to pay for the job, not the man — but they had better chances of promotion.

The origins of Hazop

In 1963 the Division was designing a plant for the production of phenol and acetone from cumene. It was a time when the aim of the Engineering Department was "minimum capital cost" (rather than minimum lifetime cost or maximum profit) and the design had been pruned of all inessential features. In the Works we felt that the pruning had gone too far. It was also a time when method study and, in particular, "critical examination" was popular. Critical examination is a formal technique for examining an activity and generating alternatives by asking "What is achieved?", "What else could be achieved?", "What should be achieved?", "How is it achieved?", "When is it achieved?", "Where is it achieved?", "Who achieves it?", and so on.

Ken Gee, now production manager, decided to see if critical examination could be applied to the design of the Phenol Plant in order to identify the deficiencies in the design. A team of three was appointed: the two senior members of the start-up team and an expert in critical examination. During 1964 they met for three full days per week for four months, examining the Phenol Plant line diagrams and covering acres of paper with the questions and answers. They discovered many potential hazards and operating problems that had not been foreseen, modifying the technique as they did so. They came up with an approach which was recognisably hazard and operability studies (Hazop) as we know it today, though it was modified during later studies. In essence, a technique designed to generate alternatives was modified so that it generated deviations.

Hazop becomes established

Hazop is applied by a team to a line diagram — that is, a diagram showing all the pipelines in a plant. For each line we ask, "Could there be no flow? If so, could it be hazardous or prevent efficient operation? If so, how could we prevent it or guard against the consequences?" Then we ask the same questions about more flow, less flow and reverse flow, about more or less temperature and pressure, about changes in composition, and so on. The technique is laborious and time-consuming but well worthwhile and has now been widely adopted.

Plants are now so complicated that we cannot see what can go wrong just by looking at the drawings. We have to go through the design in detail asking a whole series of questions about each pipeline and piece of equipment (Kletz T A, *Hazop and Hazan — Identifying and Assessing Process Industry Hazards*, Institution of Chemical Engineers, Rugby, 4th edition, 1999, Chapter 2). The technique is, of course, no more than a way of harnessing the knowledge and experience of the team in a systematic way so that as little as possible is missed. If the team lack knowledge and experience, the whole exercise is a waste of time. This is obvious but has to be stressed at a time when industry no longer considers the over-fifties as assets in which 30 years' salary has been invested but as expenses to be reduced as soon as possible.

More operating points than safety ones came out of the original study and this is often true today. The "Op" part of Hazop is as important as the "Haz" part.

I have been called, incorrectly, the father of Hazop. I was there when it was conceived and born but was too busy running the existing plants to take much interest in the new one. Later, when I took up the full-time safety job, I became an enthusiastic advocate of Hazop. The most I can claim is that, "ideas do not show themselves productive with those who suggest them or apply them for the first time, but with those persevering workers who feel them strongly and put all their faith and love in their efficacy" (Santiago Ramón y Cajol quoted by Carey J, *The Faber Book of Science*, Faber, London, 1995, p257).

A change of management

In 1963 Edward Challis left the Works to start a new Central Investigation Department. His successor had had a successful career

before and after his two and a half years on Oil Works but his management style was not suited to the Works and both it and I went through
a difficult period. The first year was not too bad, as the new manager
was busy finding out what went on, but then there were changes.

His style of management was entirely different from Edward Challis.
He tried to do as much as possible himself. He took direct charge of production matters, giving detailed instructions to the section managers,
and sometimes the plant managers. I was now in effect an assistant to
the works manager rather than an assistant works manager. Personally,
however, he was one of the nicest men I have ever worked for. He was
approachable and we had several talks on the way the job should be
run. He always agreed that I should be in charge of production, but in
practice nothing ever changed. He could not help his nature.

On one occasion he asked me to write a job description and I wrote
two. Just as light sometimes behaves as a wave and sometimes as a
stream of particles, so an assistant works manager, I suggested, is sometimes a production manager and sometimes an assistant. I had moved
from near one extreme to the other. Of course, Edward Challis often discussed problems directly with section managers, but he always kept me
in the picture. We had a long talk every evening at 5 o'clock.

Things come unstuck...

If the new style had worked it might have been tolerable, but it did not.
I thought many of the works manager's decisions were wrong; costs
rose and output fell. To give just one example, the carbonylation plants
at this time frequently developed small leaks. The works manager
favoured frequent shutdowns to put things right while I felt it was better to keep the plants on line as long as possible.

He also wasted time on unnecessary activities. Every month there
was a meeting of the whole of the senior staff at which they were invited to discuss their personal problems, not their technical ones. This
encouraged people to think up gripes they did not have. If anyone had
a real problem, the atmosphere was sufficiently relaxed for them to be
able to talk to me or the works manager, without waiting for a special
opportunity.

One evening at 5 o'clock I went in to see the works manager. I found
he had cleared his table, had had some sandwiches sent up and was

intending to stay late sorting about four hundred letters, one for each member of staff, announcing a pay rise, a job the works clerk used to do. I felt rotten going home and leaving him sorting letters until late, but the work was so absurdly unnecessary that I did not see why I should offer to help him.

Edward Challis was by now Production Manager and I wondered if I ought to talk to him and tell him why I thought the Works performance was slipping, but this was too much like disloyalty to my immediate boss. It would have been easier if he had not been a nice guy. Finally, one day in August 1965 Edward told me, as tactfully as he could, that with all the current problems it seemed the works manager and I needed some assistance. An extra assistant works manager, Rab Telfer, would join the Works and take over responsibility for operations while I would be in charge of process investigation. I was back where I was seven years earlier, though admittedly with more rank (and pay).

...and management changes

After a couple of months the works manager went on sick leave. Edward Challis was brought back for a few months and then Rab Telfer was appointed works manager. If I felt at the time that this was a personal setback, it did not turn out that way in the end. Rab Telfer was a most able man, who was to go on to become chairman of the Division. He was the fourth of that quartet of able men who influenced me greatly (the others being Bill Price, Henry Simpson and Edward Challis) and it was a privilege to work with him and watch his ways. He had all Edward Challis' qualities — personal charm, energy, technical ability, the capacity to see the essence of a problem — and more besides. Unlike Edward he was able to survey the whole area of his responsibilities systematically and handle masses of detail. He did not just look at the bulges; he looked at everything and saw the bulges before they grew.

John Cullen returned to the Works to replace Rab as assistant works manager.

A fatal accident on my patch

Before I continue with the story I want to go back to the day when Edward Challis told me that I was being pushed aside. Although he told me tactfully, he picked an unfortunate day, though he probably had no

61

choice as the official announcement was imminent. About 5 o'clock that morning the telephone had rung — nothing very unusual about that — but this time the shift manager had to tell me the one thing that every manager dreads, a fatal accident to one of those responsible to him, the only time this happened to me.

In later years I used this accident to illustrate various principles of accident investigation and therefore it is worth describing it in some detail. A suspended catalyst was removed from a process stream in a pressure filter (Figure 5.1). When a batch had been filtered, the inlet valve was closed and the liquid in the filter blown out with steam. The steam supply was then isolated, the pressure blown off through the vent and the fall in pressure observed on a pressure gauge. The operator then opened the filter for cleaning. The filter door was held closed by eight

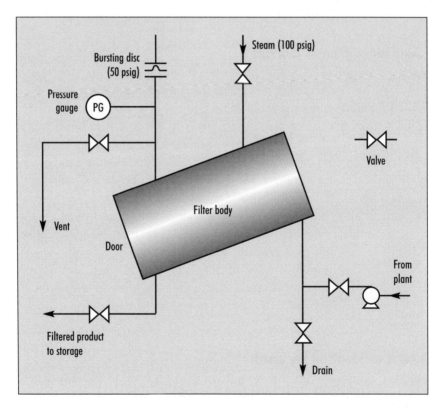

Figure 5.1: The pressure filter

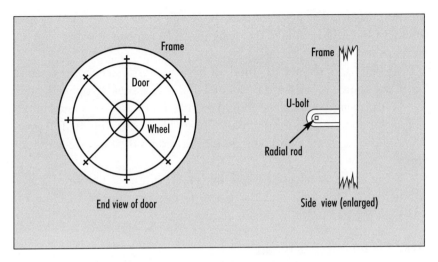

Figure 5.2: The filter door and fastening

radial bars that fitted into U-bolts on the filter body. To withdraw the radial bars from the U-bolts and open the door the operator had to turn a large wheel, fixed to the door. The door, with filter leaves attached, could then be withdrawn (Figure 5.2).

How the accident happened

One day an operator, a conscientious man of great experience, started to open the door before blowing off the pressure. He was standing in front of it and was crushed between the door and part of the structure and was killed instantly. At the time it seemed reasonable to say that the accident was due to an error by the operator. It showed the need for other operators to remain alert and to follow the operating instructions exactly. Only minor changes were made to the design. The pressure gauge and vent valve, originally located on the floor above, were moved so that they were visible to the operator when he was about to open the door. In addition, the handle on the door was modified so that the operator did not have to stand in front of the door to open it.

Several years later, when I was involved full-time on safety, I realised that inevitably, sooner or later, an operator will forget that he has not opened the vent valve and will try to open the filter while it is still under pressure. The accident was the result of the work situation, and changes should be made to the design so as to remove or reduce opportunities for error. In this case:

(a) interlocks should be fitted so that the vessel cannot be opened until the source of pressure is isolated and the vent valve opened, and

(b) the design of the door should be such that it can be opened about a quarter of an inch (6 mm) while still capable of carrying the full pressure and a separate operation should be required to release the door fully.

If the cover is released while the vessel is under pressure, this is immediately apparent and the pressure can be allowed to blow off through the gap or the door can be resealed.

Was the operator to blame?

The accident occurred at the end of the night shift, an hour before the operator was due to start his annual holiday. His mind may not have been fully on the job; he may have been thinking of his holiday. Who can blame him? It is not very helpful to say that the accident was due to human failing. We all have moments when for one reason or another our minds are not on the job and we forget a step in a routine task. This is inevitable. We should list as the cause of an accident only those features we can do something about. In this case the accident could have been prevented by better design of the equipment.

Many similar accidents have occurred when operators have had to open up equipment that has been under pressure. In contrast, every day, in every factory, equipment that has been under pressure is opened up for repair but this is normally done under a permit-to-work system. One man prepares the equipment and issues a permit to another man who opens it up, normally by carefully slackening bolts in case there is any pressure left inside. Safety is obtained by following procedures. The involvement of two people and the issue of a permit provides an opportunity to check that everything necessary has been done. Accidents are liable to happen when the same person prepares the equipment and opens it up and in these cases we need additional safety features. (The accident is described in greater detail in my book *An Engineer's View of Human Error*, 3rd edition, Institution of Chemical Engineers, Rugby, 2000, Section 2.2.1.)

Of course, we can rely on the operator to open a valve correctly 99 times out of 100, perhaps more, perhaps less if stress and distraction are high. But one failure in a hundred, or even in a thousand, is far too high when we are dealing with an operation which is carried out every day and where failure can have serious results.

Looking after the injured

Another man was seriously injured in the same accident. He was just passing by and was splashed with a corrosive chemical when the filter door flew open. As usual on such, fortunately rare, occasions a company car collected his wife every day — he lived 20 miles away — took her to the hospital and then took her home again. This amazed the injured steelworker in the next bed.

Men who had been injured at work were sometimes reluctant to claim compensation for injury or lost pay in case it hindered their chances of promotion. In such cases I had to assure them, through their foremen, that this was not the case. I emphasised to young managers that it was their responsibility to see that any of their men injured in an accident got a fair deal and that it was not one of their duties for look for reasons that might justify the company paying less than the normal tariff. Discussing this once with a manager from another company, he said that while he agreed in principle, unfortunately his company's insurers took a different view. I thought this was a pretty weak excuse. Companies can choose their insurers.

Nitrogen blanketing of flammable liquids

The period from August 1965 to about October 1966, when I was looking after process investigation, was not very satisfying as I did not feel extended. However, I used some of the time to deepen my growing interest in safety and extend my knowledge. Safety is, of course, one of every manager's responsibilities but I had taken a little more interest than some of my contemporaries, as the subject interested me and it was something the last works manager had been willing to leave to me. However, at the time I did not look upon it as a technical job. An explosion that occurred in September 1966, fortunately without injuring anyone, made me realise even more than the filter accident that new approaches were needed.

When the Works was built in 1935, provision was made for nitrogen blanketing of fixed roof storage tanks containing petrol and other light hydrocarbons. It was a forward-looking decision for the time, but the system had fallen into disuse. About 1963 the system had been put back into use and arrangements made to extend it to a part of the Works that was not covered. The detailed design of the system was unusual. All the storage tanks were connected to a nitrogen gasholder. If the level in a tank rose nitrogen was pushed into the gasholder. If the level fell, nitrogen was drawn from it. This system was installed because in 1935 nitrogen was expensive and it was necessary to conserve it. In later designs each tank was blanketed separately and when the level in it rose the nitrogen was vented to atmosphere, together with some hydrocarbon vapour. (In recent years common vent systems have come back into favour, in order to reduce or prevent the venting of hydrocarbons to atmosphere.)

Why protective equipment needs regular checking

Despite the nitrogen blanketing, in 1966 an explosion in a tank blew the roof off and was followed by a fire. It burned for three hours as the Fire Service had to bring a large monitor (a "gun" for delivering foam) from their headquarters at Durham, 30 miles away. After the fire, it was found that the tank had been disconnected from the nitrogen gasholder. The plant manager had checked that it was connected seven months earlier when the tank had changed duty, but no-one had checked since then. It was as well that the tank had been disconnected. Further checks showed that the "nitrogen" in the gasholder and storage tanks contained 15% oxygen as there were leaks in the system and no regular analyses. If the tank had been connected to the gasholder the explosion might have spread to all the tanks.

This incident taught me, and many others, that all protective equipment has to be checked regularly. The equipment was not the most modern, but it was adequate if used properly. I have discussed this fire on many occasions with groups of managers, designers and maintenance engineers and it is surprising how many want to redesign the system and install more and better equipment. But if people do not use the equipment they have got, will they use new equipment? The incident disclosed not only a poor method of working — no inspection — but also a failure of training. As managers we had failed to convince the foremen and operators that nitrogen blanketing was necessary. They had looked on it as something of marginal importance — an optional extra — something to bother with if you have time but something you can afford to ignore if you are busy.

The source of ignition was never found with certainty but this is common in reports on fires. Possible causes are discussed in my book *Learning from Accidents* (2nd edition, Butterworth-Heinemann, Oxford, 1994, Chapter 4). The incident also taught me that we can never be 100% certain that we have removed all sources of ignition and we should therefore prevent the formation of explosive mixtures of flammable vapour and air. Or use equipment that can withstand an explosion.

More incidents and reactions

The lessons of the tank fire were reinforced a few weeks later when there was an explosion in a flare stack. It was used intermittently and there was supposed to be a flow of nitrogen up the stack to prevent air diffusing down and to sweep away any small leaks of air that occurred. The nitrogen flow had been reduced almost to zero, to save nitrogen. It was not measured and the atmosphere in the stack was never analysed.

These various incidents taught me that in matters of safety, instructions are not enough. You have to explain to people why you consider an instruction important, and you have to check that it is being followed.

As a plant manager I was always looking in eyewash bottle cabinets, trying out safety showers, checking the permit for a maintenance job, and so on. I continued to do so on my plant tours. A ticked sheet from someone else does not prove that everything is OK. If you never look yourself it shows that you don't consider the job important and if you don't, why should anyone else? Sometimes I asked an operator to demonstrate that he could use breathing apparatus. He always could. (Even today, if I visit a plant, I have to restrain myself as my first reaction is to poke and pry in all the corners.) The two explosions showed me that I would have to extend my curiosity to a whole range of technical matters. Many of them could not, of course, be checked visually. It was necessary to ask to see analysis results, test reports and so on.

A technique which I started to use at this time was to go round with a camera photographing hazards and then showing them to a staff meeting. It woke people up to see on a screen a hazard they passed every day without noticing. (A safety officer on another works who tried this technique, however, found it less successful. The works manager who was present when the slides were shown was so shocked by what he saw that he lost his temper, and tore strips of all the managers present.) I also started to build up a library of slides illustrating accidents that have occurred. Some have been used in the Institution of Chemical Engineers' Interactive Training Packages — but most, I have been told — have laid unused in cupboards at Wilton since I retired.

Management science

About this time the Division's Management Services Department (MSD) came in for a lot of criticism. It was supposed to be a centre of expertise which could apply the latest management techniques to the solution of the Division's problems. In practice it was used as a source of spare manpower. If a department had a problem but insufficient resources to investigate it, they gave it to MSD. They got all the dull problems and all the unsolvable ones, so how could they shine? (In contrast, the Central Investigation Department, set up under Edward Challis to investigate major technical problems, investigated those that they thought most important.) The director responsible, Harry North, who knew me well as he was previously production director, asked me to chair a small committee to examine these criticisms. It was packed with members of MSD, in order not to offend them, so obviously our report could not be too critical. Our main recommendation was that MSD should pay more attention to the financial returns before allocating staff to their client's problems. One member of the committee later succeeded Harry North. He drew his sword and made short work of MSD. Its rise and fall is described in *The Awakening Giant* (Blackwell, Oxford, 1985, Chapter 7) by Andrew Pettigrew.

Accident statistics

Another committee that I served on at this time — being no longer involved with day-to-day production problems, I could be spared for committee chores — was an inter-divisional committee (or working party or task force: the company was always finding new names for committees to make them seem less of a stick-in-the-mud way of tack-ling problems) on accident statistics. The lost-time accident rate, the usual measure of performance, was easily fiddled. It was the practice at the time to try to persuade injured men to come into work, even if they had to just sit in an office, so that the accident did not count. A better statistic was wanted. We recommended a figure based on the number of accidents which the Medical Department certified as being above a cer-tain degree of severity. The system was already in use in some Divisions but our recommendation was not adopted as some medical officers refused to co-operate.

While the committee was formulating its ideas I discussed them with a some of the works managers at Wilton and Billingham. To my surprise the chairman of the committee, a Dyestuffs Division works manager and future chairman, got rather upset at what he called "pre-mature disclosure". I pointed out that we were not planning a war or a take-over but making reasonable proposals to reasonable men. All our management training had emphasised that one should never present people, at any level, with finished proposals but involve them in their development. If they feel they have been involved and consulted they are more likely to accept them. This rather trivial incident shows how skin-deep is the commitment of many managers to management theo-ries. They have been on courses and read books and can say all the right things but once they are under the slightest pressure, a breath of criti-cism perhaps, it all disappears.

Away from work

By 1958 most of my friends had been married for several years. Once I reached thirty some of my female relatives started introducing me to eli-gible girls. Sometimes it was done quite tactfully: "We are having some friends to lunch on Sunday. Would you like to join us?" (Lunch, note, not dinner, in the hope that I would feel like a walk in the afternoon.) At other times the intention was made quite clear from the start. In 1958 I met Denise through one of these introductions; we were engaged with-in two months and married six months later, a few days after my 36th birthday, soon after my return to Oil Works. She was a speech therapist and 12 years younger than I was.

Our first son was born in 1961 and the second in 1963. Our elder son used to tease me that I was older than any of his friends' fathers but I have remained active professionally long after the others have retired.

When the second baby arrived I agreed with my wife that she would go to him if needed during the night and I would go to the elder one. So far he had rarely disturbed us at night. All this soon changed and for over a year I was up every night in the middle of the night, often for an hour or so. If my wife went instead, he wanted Daddy. He had got used to me as the "night shift operator". I could have done without this at a time when I was coping with a difficult works manager on the day shift.

Historians now describe the 1960s as a decade of substantial change, when old taboos gave way to new freedoms. "What was it like", young readers may ask, "to live through such times?" The answer is that, like most people, I never realised I was living in a time of change. I was too busy with my family and career to notice. Gradual change is seen only in retrospect, not while it is happening.

6

MANPOWER UTILISATION

Lines of demarcation and other restrictive practices are property rights. Like the ownership of land they are held as a defence against changing economic conditions and are characterised by hair-splitting and legalistic distinctions, they will be sold if the price is right but the right to own them is jealousy guarded. Unlike property rights, they are not enforced by the law.

Notes on a talk by Llywelyn Jones at Billingham, 1967

After a year on process investigation work I had another move. I was put in charge of a small Works team that was looking at ways of improving productivity.

During the 1950s work measurement was used as a tool for improving productivity. The work a man did was measured — usually by work study officers with stop watches (Sir John Harvey-Jones, ICI Chairman from 1982, started his ICI career on such a job) — and a bonus was paid if it exceeded a standard amount.

By the mid-1960s the whole procedure had become a farce. Bonuses hardly varied from week to week. The system had outlived its usefulness and a new approach was needed.

Wrestling with productivity

ICI and the unions agreed a scheme called "Manpower Utilisation and Payment Structure" or MUPS. In exchange for a substantial increase in pay (about 30%) weekly-paid employees would accept a lower degree of supervision and would carry out tasks previously carried out by members of other unions. In particular, it was hoped that the craft unions would allow general workers to carry out simple maintenance tasks. MUPS was to be tried out on several sites, following local agreement on the details. In practice, only two sites were initially successful. Joe Roeber has described the results achieved, there and elsewhere, in *Social Change at Work* (Duckworth, London, 1975).

Oil Works was not a trial site but in the enthusiasm of the early days everyone hoped that MUPS would take off soon and a team was set up to prepare for the great day. My colleagues included Joe Heaton, a mechanical engineer (and one of the few successful "manageers" — see page 22), and a large contingent from the Management Services Department. We had to estimate how many people were really needed to run the Works and how we could motivate them to adopt a staff rather than an "us-and-them" attitude. "Job enrichment" was one of the vogue phrases of the period.

There was much interest in the factors that motivated people and, in particular, in the work of Frederick Hertzberg who stressed the importance of growth, achievement, responsibility and recognition. He was modest compared with some of the "management science" people, as shown by the Preface to his *Work and the Nature of Man* (Staples Press, London, 1968):

> The fact is that the increase in profits that the psychologists can effect at any one time is slight in comparison with the effects of the engineers, marketing experts and sales department.

I attended many courses at this time, mainly to bring me up-to-date on management theory. The one that most influenced me was two days on public speaking as it was 100% relevant to my needs. Too many courses fail because people are sent on them and yet they feel no need of them. Adults (perhaps children also) learn only when they feel a need to learn.

Understanding the union view

Throughout 1967 I spent almost all my working hours talking, writing and thinking about MUPS and came to appreciate, more clearly than before, the underlying reasons for many union attitudes. In a note I wrote at the time, I tried to show that lines of demarcation are property rights and are defended with the same strength of feeling as others defend their right to hold land.

This note was well-received but another one less so. Irritated by the Personnel Department, with which I did not always agree, I wrote an anonymous note parodying one of their points of view, that supervisors should be weekly-paid employees. I suggested that personnel officers should also be weekly paid staff. I sent the note to a number of people who I thought might appreciate the humour.

By chance, Joe Heaton was visiting the Personnel Department when the note arrived. Instead of smiling and tossing it aside, as I expected, the senior members of the department got very worked up and rushed around saying "Very embarrassing"; "Who could have written it?" "Have the directors seen it?" "What will they think?" Joe and I kept a low profile for a few weeks.

Time for another change

After a year on MUPS, by the autumn of 1967 it was clear that its implementation on Oil Works, and in the whole of the North-East, was going to be long delayed and that we had done most that we could usefully do in the meantime. I told the works manager, Rab Telfer, that there wasn't a job and that I would welcome a move. It was 16 years since I joined Oil Works and although I had had a two-year break in Technical Department I felt I had been long enough in one department. When I joined the Works I had felt that some of the long-serving managers were too ready to condemn a foreman by quoting errors he had made 10 or 15 years before. I was beginning to do the same myself. At the age of 46, it was time to move.

As well as the incidents described earlier there had been several other serious accidents in the Division; five men had been killed in three fires on North Tees Works in the period 1965-7. Figure 6.1 (on page 74) shows how ICI's fatal accident rate had deteriorated. Ken Gee, now Production Director, convinced the Board that there was a need for a technical input to safety, that it could no longer be left to arts graduates, retired soldiers or elderly foremen. The attitude to safety had not changed since I was a part-time safety officer 13 years earlier. I was asked if I was interested in the new appointment and was also asked to write a job description. I did so, describing what Rab called a "coat" that fitted me perfectly, and on 1 January 1968 I moved into the Division HQ as its first technical safety adviser.

If I had been appointed to a full-time job in safety only few years earlier I would have wondered what I had done wrong. But times had changed and the tag-along (see the quotation at the beginning of Chapter 5, p46) was now accepted.

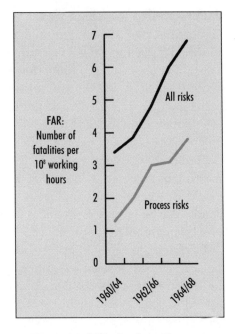

Figure 6.1: ICI's fatal accident rate (FAR — the number of fatal accidents in 10^8 working hours or in a group of 1000 men in a working lifetime) expressed as a five-year moving average

The end of MUPS

Before I leave Oil Works, readers may like to know the end of the MUPS story. Renamed WSA (Weekly Staff Agreement) it was finally implemented throughout ICI in the early 1970s. At a few sites there were real improvements in attitudes and productivity. At Billingham and Wilton nothing much changed. Payroll employees were called "staff (weekly-paid)", and got the increase in pay but only very minor changes were made in working practices, though there was some reduction in supervision. Monthly-paid staff had to be given a similar increase in pay to preserve differentials and to justify this a Staff Development Programme (SDP) was instituted. People were expected to demonstrate increases in productivity and responsibility. A lot of effort was put into proving that they had increased but nothing much really changed. No wonder the wags said that SDP meant Slows Down Progress while WSA meant Work Stops Altogether. Ten years later, in the early 1980s, far greater reductions in manning were achieved without increases in pay when a severe recession hit ICI.

Everyone agrees that we should have one grade of employee and no longer divide people into staff and payroll (or workers). By calling everyone staff we thought everyone would be treated like staff used to be treated. As mentioned in Chapter 2, we ought to have foreseen that in the long run the result would be the opposite, that conditions of employment for everyone would be closer to those of the majority, the former payroll, that there would be levelling down as well as levelling up. Professional staff in many companies, including ICI, now have less security of employment than payroll had in the 1960s.

7

SAFETY ADVISER — PART 1

*There does seem to be a moment when you realize that,
quite by accident, you happen to have come on the stage at
exactly the moment you were expected. Everything is
arranged for you — waiting for you.*

Katherine Mansfield, *Bliss and Other Stories*
(Constable, London, 1920)

My remit, as Division Safety Adviser, was to advise design and operating staff on the action they should take to avoid accidents and dangerous occurrences. This was a very broad one and I soon set myself several guidelines that I followed for the rest of my ICI career.

My job guidelines
(1) I decided to concentrate on the technical accidents — mainly fires and explosions — rather than on mechanical accidents — slips, falls and so on. The mechanical accidents were (and still are) the more numerous, but the fires and explosions caused the worst sort of injury, half the deaths, material damage and loss of production. I had not forgotten the injured men I saw in hospital after the 1957 fire.

There were also site safety officers at both Billingham and Wilton and individual works safety officers who were quite capable of looking after the everyday hazards, and dealing with factory inspectors and shop stewards, but no-one else was able or willing to take a full-time interest in the technical hazards.

Even today there are many companies where the safety officer and the senior managers worry only about the lost-time accident rate and take little or no interest in technical safety (alias loss prevention, alias, in the chemical industry, process safety).

(2) I tried to keep a sense of balance, concentrating on the most probable or serious hazards, and advising people not to spend time and money dealing with unlikely or trivial ones. I developed numerical criteria to help us decide which risks should be dealt with urgently and which could be ignored, at least for the time being. There is more on this subject later.

(3) I tried to sell my ideas softly but persistently. I had no authority to impose my ideas nor did I wish for any. A manager must remain in control of his plant. I tried to convince managers and designers, by technical arguments, that they should incorporate certain ideas or practices into their plants. I was helped by the fact that my boss, Ken Gee, and later Edward Challis who succeeded him as Production Director, were known to support my approach. To help get my ideas across I started a monthly *Safety Newsletter* and a regular series of discussions, described later.

In later years I tried to emphasise to my staff that a job was not finished when they made their recommendations. It was not finished until the manager or designer concerned had carried them out or had persuaded them to change their recommendation.

(4) As far as possible, if I had an idea, I just got on with it, rather than asking if I should. I did not ask permission to start a monthly *Safety Newsletter* or weekly safety discussions or if I should set numerical criteria for safety. I did not ask the Board, for example, to agree that combustible gas detectors should be widely installed on our plants for the detection of leaks. Instead I persuaded individual managers or designers that it was the right solution for their particular problem and gradually it became the accepted practice — the common law of the Division.

To quote my former colleague, Derek Birchall (*Chemistry and Industry*, 18 July 1983, p539),

The reason for the speed and success of the industrial revolution in this country was largely the fact that many of the inventors did not need to seek support, but simply got on with it. Abraham Darby did not have to write a submission in order to attempt the experiment of using coke rather than charcoal in iron smelting — he was master of his own experiment and of its consequences.

Benefiting from the ICI style

People from other companies have sometimes been surprised that the Division had no central committee determining safety policy and that I just got on with things, but this was the ICI style (see Appendix to Chapter 9 on page 123). If one asked permission there was a 50% chance that it would be refused, or a decision postponed for further consideration. If one just got on with it, 19 times out of 20 nothing was said. On the odd occasion when I told a works managers' meeting of an intention, one works manager had reservations and the Production Director would urge caution and delay. It was better to tell the meeting what I had done, not what I was going to do.

Sir Kenneth Hutchison (*High Speed Gas — An Autobiography*, Duckworth, London, 1987, p75) has described how in 1927 the publication of Walker, Lewis and McAdam's treatise on chemical engineering opened his eyes to the value of the methods used in America for improving chemical processes. By 1968 these methods were standard but had hardly been applied to safety or loss prevention in the UK. There had been so little systematic thinking that it was hardly possible not to make an impression. Wherever one looked there were problems worthy of investigation. In many cases it was obvious what should be done but people were not getting on with it, through lack of determination, lack of resources, or ignorance of the hazard. The next section provides an example of what I mean.

An accident during maintenance

About a year before I was appointed three men had been killed in a serious fire on North Tees Works. A fitter was opening up a pump when hot oil, above its auto-ignition temperature, came out and caught fire. The plant was destroyed. Examination of the wreckage showed that the suction valve on the pump had been left open. The supervisor who issued the permit-to-work said that he had inspected the pump and found the valve already shut, the pump having been left standing ready for repair over the weekend. Either the supervisor's recollection was incorrect, and he had not checked the valve, or after he had checked it, someone else opened it. Either way, the system of working was poor and after the fire instructions were issued that in future:

- All valves isolating equipment under repair must be locked shut with a padlock and chain (or equally effective means).
- In addition, equipment under repair must also be isolated by slip-plates (spades) or physical disconnection unless the job to be done was so quick that fitting slip-plates would take as long and be as dangerous as the main job. Valves must be locked shut while slip-plates are fitted.

In North Tees Works the fire had been so traumatic that everyone accepted these new requirements without hesitation, but were they really being followed in the rest of the Division? Was it possible to follow them? Were they followed elsewhere? And would they be followed in a few years' time when memories had faded?

Improving maintenance procedures

I visited plants, looked at permits-to-work and at actual isolations, and found that on the whole the new rules were followed, though sometimes people were not clear precisely what they should be doing. However, I found other things wrong. Although isolation was, on the whole, satisfactory, identification was poor. Maintenance workers sometimes opened up the wrong equipment. I had a long struggle to persuade Olefine Works in particular that equipment under repair, if not permanently labelled, should be identified by a numbered tag. Oil Works had started tagging a few years earlier.

To fit slip-plates plants have to be designed so that there is room for the slip-plate and this meant convincing the design department that they should design accordingly. This was not difficult as my Oil Works colleague Joe Heaton was now in charge of piping design. Other Divisions knew little of the North Tees fire and had not changed their standards. Incredibly, no report on the fire for general circulation had been issued. I wrote one, drawing heavily on the Works internal report.

I found an old report in the Billingham files describing a similar incident 30 years earlier and making similar recommendations. This and other repeated accidents led me to a theme that I have continued to emphasise in presentations, articles and a book (*Lessons from Disaster — How Organisations have No Memory and Accidents Recur*, Institution of Chemical Engineers, Rugby, 1993): organisations have no memory; only people have memories and after a while they leave, taking their memories with them.

Keeping the organisation's memory fresh

How could we make sure the lessons of the fire were not forgotten again? I kept up regular inspections of permits-to-work, later passing them on to my colleague, Eric Hunt. But this was not enough. It is not sufficient to check that rules are being followed or people will stop following them as soon as attention decreases. We have to convince people that they should be followed. I started a series of discussions on the causes of accidents that were to continue for the rest of my ICI career, and afterwards.

Each week I invited between 12 and 20 people, nominated by their departments, to attend a morning discussion. I described an accident, briefly, and illustrated it by slides. The group then questioned me to find out the rest of the facts, the facts that *they thought* important and that they wanted to know. They then said what *they thought* ought to be done to prevent similar incidents happening again. Because they were involved in a discussion, the audience remembered more than if I had lectured to them and they more were committed to the conclusions, as they were *their* conclusions.

After the discussion we had lunch together and any queries on safety could be raised with me. When we had our periodic economy campaigns a few people wondered if I should give a free lunch every week for 12 to 20 people but I pointed out that it was worth the cost if we got an hour's extra work from those who came.

During my first discussions, about half the morning was taken up with the North Tees fire and the other half with other incidents involving preparation for maintenance. The people attending were mainly managers, maintenance engineers and design engineers (of all levels) with the

Harland Frank, 1977   *Edward Challis, 1973*

Frank Lees, 1993   *Jim McQuaid, 1977*

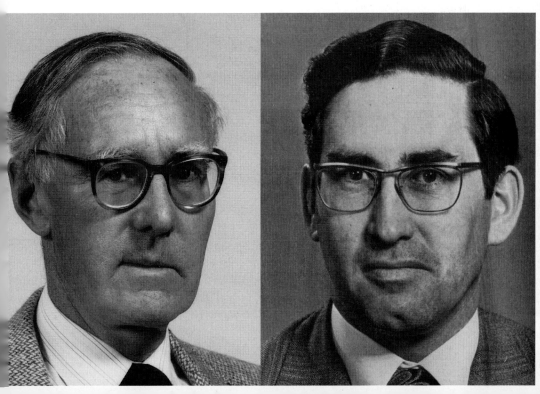

My wife Denise with our two boys, 1965

My parents, my two sons and me, 1969

ICI's new technical safety adviser, January 1968

The Wilton site, 1974: my office was in the complex in the foreground

Denise and me, 1979, celebrating 35 years' service with ICI. A year later I was a widower.

At my desk in Billingham before the move to Wilton, 1974

Robed for my DSc degree at Loughborough, 1986

Collecting the insignia of my OBE, 1997: with (l to r) my elder son Anthony, my sister Sonia and my younger son Nigel

Opening the Astra Charnwood pilot plant, 1998

occasional foreman. I tried to encourage works to hold similar discussions for foremen and operators, with varying success. For several months an Oil Works assistant foreman with an aptitude for training was seconded to me and went round the works holding such discussions.

Improving the value of group discussions

The origin of these discussions dates back to my time in Oil Works. I had built up a library of slides illustrating accidents that had happened, and from time to time I showed them to the staff. One day the Division's training manager said to me, "Instead of telling them what happened, why don't you let them work it out". Like a single stone setting off a landslide, this single remark changed the way I tackled many problems (see Chapter 3, pages 25 and 26 for another example).

Each year I changed the content of the discussions and occasionally revived the old ones for the benefit of new recruits. As I mentioned on page 68, many of the slides and notes I used were later published by the Institution of Chemical Engineers as their Interactive Training Packages and are still included in the current editions.

I have wandered a long way since I started my discussion of the North Tees fire, but I wanted to show how a single incident, if followed up thoroughly in all its implications, can keep one busy for a long time. Unfortunately, accident investigations are often superficial, dealing only with the obvious technical recommendations but not with the underlying causes. It is easy to recommend a few changes to plant design or operating methods. It is much more difficult to accept that extensive changes may have to be made to the way activities are carried out and that extensive training or inspection programmes may be necessary. Furthermore, major incidents are soon forgotten once the initial excitement is over. My views on the preparation of equipment for maintenance are described in greater detail in *Handbook of Highly Toxic Materials Handling and Management*, edited by Grossel S S and Crowl D A, Dekker, New York, 1995, Chapter 5 and *What Went Wrong? — Case Histories of Process Plant Disasters*, 4th edition, Gulf, Houston, Texas, 1998, Chapter 1.

The control of modifications is another example of a situation where changes in procedures, training and follow-up were all needed (see page 45).

By Accident

The Polythene Plant explosion

A year after my appointment as safety adviser there was a serious explosion on the Polythene (polyethylene) Plant at Wilton, which killed four men. Although this plant belonged to Plastics Division, at the request of John Harvey-Jones, at the time a deputy chairman of Heavy Organic Chemicals (HOC) Division with particular responsibility for the Wilton site, I was included in the investigating team. The investigations taught me a lot.

The immediate cause of the explosion was a leak of ethylene from a badly-made joint, ignited by an unknown cause. However, there was much more to it than that. Examination of records showed that leaks were common but no-one really worried as they did not expect them to ignite. How could they when all sources of ignition were removed? In HOC Division, a hundred yards away, everyone accepted that it is impossible to eliminate all sources of ignition and therefore leaks should be prevented and, if they do occur, allowed to disperse by open construction and natural ventilation. This was one of the lessons of the fire in Oil Works in 1957, described in Chapter 4. Much of the Polythene Plant equipment was indoors and the leak — a few tens of kilograms — would not have mattered out of doors where several tonnes are needed for an explosion.

How could people in the same company, on the same site, many of them meeting socially at lunch every day, hold dramatically opposed views on a technical matter of such importance? The Polythene Plant, though operated by Plastics Division, had until a few years before been operated by Alkali Division and the staff retained something of the aloof, self-confident, patrician attitude which was said to characterise that Division (see Chapter 2, page 9). What could they hope to learn from the plebs in HOC Division? There was something of a monastic attitude about the Polythene Plant. The explosion, besides demolishing a compressor house, blew down the monastery walls.

Inbred attitudes

The Polythene Plant attitude is not uncommon. All large organisations — or parts of large organisations — can become very inbred, too self-reliant, unwilling or unable to find out what goes on in the outer darkness beyond their boundaries. There was something of this attitude

82

years later at Bhopal when over 2000 people were killed in 1984 by a leak of methyl isocyanate (MIC) from a storage tank on a Union Carbide plant. Afterwards Union Carbide (and other companies) greatly reduced or eliminated their storage capacity for MIC and other toxic intermediates. But for ten years before Bhopal some of us had been stressing the need to reduce inventories in plants and storage areas — "What you don't have, can't leak". I doubt if those concerned in Union Carbide had even heard of this phrase, or the concept of "inherently safer plants" which springs from it.

We never found the source of ignition on the Polythene Plant. It may have been badly maintained electrical equipment or it may have been static electricity from a leak, accumulating on a piece of unearthed metal and then discharging to earth. As noted in Chapter 5, sources of ignition are often never found as so little energy is needed to ignite a mixture of flammable gas or vapour and air. The energy released when a 1p coin falls 1 cm is sufficient, if concentrated into a spark or speck of hot metal.

More lessons from the Polythene Plant explosion

There were many other lessons for HOC Division from the explosion, most of them repeating the lessons learnt 12 years earlier:

- The need for open construction. We pulled down the brick walls of a new compressor house that had just been built. HOC Division usually built open plants but this one was enclosed to reduce noise radiation. Another solution — acoustic insulation — was found to the noise problem. Unfortunately in recent years enclosed compressor houses have again been built in order to reduce the outside noise.
- The need for regular inspections of electrical equipment, and of all safety equipment, reinforcing the messages of the tank fire and explosion on Oil Works in 1966 (see Chapter 3, page 65).
- The need for gas detectors, so that leaks are detected as soon as they occur, and emergency valves for the rapid isolation of leaks.
- The need to monitor workmanship and follow up weak points. After the explosion, leak rates on the polythene plants came down dramatically.

I was busy spreading these messages round the Division when my attention was diverted by a second serious incident.

The Nylon Works fire

In 1968 people wondered why Wilton had a better safety record than Billingham. The Wilton site had been in operation for 17 years and the fatal accident rate was lower than on the older site north of the River Tees. In six months the position reversed. In May 1969, five months after the polythene explosion, two men were killed and several seriously burned in a fire on Nylon Works, operated by Dyestuffs Division. The plant involved, the cyclohexane oxidation plant, was similar to that involved in the Flixborough explosion six years later (see Chapter 8), though the two incidents had little else in common.

The immediate cause of the Nylon Works fire was similar to that of the North Tees fire (see page 78), an error in the preparation of equipment for maintenance. Part of the plant consisted of two parallel streams; the rest was a single stream. One of the parallel streams was being maintained, separated by slip-plates from the rest of the plant which was on line. One of the slip-plates, on a little-used line, was missing and four tons of hot flammable liquid, similar to petrol, leaked out and caught fire. The fire spread rapidly as the layout was congested and open drains allowed the spillage to spread quickly. We were lucky there were not more casualties as 80 maintenance workers, in addition to the normal operating team, were present on the plant at the time. I was again involved in the investigation and, again, there was much more to the story.

More cultural problems

Why was the engineering design so poor of the cyclohexane unit so poor? Dyestuffs Division's expertise lay in batch processing. As nylon production grew, continuous plants became necessary. Dyestuffs hired contractors and left it to them. They got a good process design but a disgracefully poor engineering design. If they had asked HOC Division for advice they would have been told to watch the contractors closely, tell them in detail the standards to adopt and vet their designs thoroughly. They would have been told to avoid, if possible, maintaining a major part of the plant while the rest was online but, if this was essential, to separate to two halves and to plan at the design stage how to isolate the two parts. It should not have been left to a foreman to sort out a few days before the shutdown.

If the Plastics team were monks, the Dyestuffs team were amateurs. It provided another example of different Divisions with the same problems adopting quite different solutions.

How the Divisions coped

At Nylon Works the source of ignition was discovered and caused a lot of interest. A diesel engine, used by the maintenance team, sucked in leaking cyclohexane vapour and began to race. The driver tried to stop it by shutting off the fuel but this had no effect as the fuel was entering the engine through the air inlet. Finally flash back occurred, igniting the cyclohexane vapour and the fire spread to a pool of liquid. Before this, the fact that diesel engines could ignite flammable vapour was not widely known.

Plastics Division management told other polythene manufacturers about the explosion but otherwise tried to give their fire as little publicity as possible, on the grounds that the type of joint that had leaked and many other circumstances were peculiar to polythene. In contrast, Dyestuffs Division were very open about their fire — or at least the source of ignition. A press release was issued and reports appeared in many journals. They successfully deflected interest away from the aspects that they had not handled very well. no-one asked why the leak occurred.

On other occasions companies have been more open about an accident when the cause was an unusual phenomenon they could not reasonably be expected to know about. Such accidents are rare. Most accidents are due to a failure to apply well-known principles or knowledge.

Again there were lessons for my own Division from the Nylon Works fire and these had to be made known. I started a second series of case history discussions, this time covering the Polythene Plant explosion and the Nylon Works fire. For some months I was spending two mornings per week on these discussions, one at Wilton and one at Billingham. Hundreds of managers and designers attended, in groups of twenty or so, and others that I was to hold in future years, so that gradually they had an effect on the thinking of the Division and, to a lesser extent, on that of the Wilton site. I held a special discussion in the Staff Club at 6 pm one day for those senior managers who were too busy (they said) to spare the time during the day.

Investigating static electricity

In 1968, soon after I was appointed, the North Tees Works manager
asked for help with a survey of electrostatic hazards. Static electricity is
developed when one phase moves in contact with another, for example,
when liquid flows through a pipe or is splashed into a tank. One charge
appears on the liquid and an equal and opposite charge on the container. If the liquid is conducting and the container is earthed there is no
problem as the charges leak away very quickly. However, pure hydrocarbons are non-conducting and the charges leak away only slowly. A
spark is liable to occur between the liquid and any earthed metal near-
by and ignite any flammable mixture of vapour and air that is present.

North Tees handled large amounts of flammable hydrocarbons. The
Works manager was not sure what hazards he had and what he ought
to be doing about them. I arranged for a member of the Research
Department, Eric Hunt, to be seconded to the Works for several months
to survey these hazards, under my direction, and recommend action. I
then suggested to the Oil and Olefine Works managers that they should
do the same on their works and they readily agreed. Eric then returned
to Research Department.

Surveying other hazards

After the Polythene Plant explosion it became clear that many other
hazards would benefit from similar systematic and thorough surveys.
Following the explosion there was little difficulty recruiting extra staff
for safety and I was able to arrange for Eric to join me permanently. For
many years, until his retirement, he spent most of his time out on the
plant looking at the testing of alarms and trips, the standard of maintenance of classified electrical equipment (that is, electrical equipment for
use in flammable atmospheres), permits-to-work (looking at the job as
well as the paperwork), sample points, sight glasses, escape routes and
other hazards or types of protective equipment. We called these investigations surveys to distinguish them from the more conventional safety
audits which involve a quick look at everything.

Our surveys were very thorough. When Eric surveyed trip and
alarm testing, for example, he personally witnessed the testing of every
trip and alarm in the Division and checked that the faults found were
promptly repaired. He made many detailed recommendations on indi-

vidual installations and many valuable general recommendations. I have no doubt that, provided the subjects are well chosen, surveying contributes more to safety per man-year of effort than conventional auditing.

Surveying (or auditing) can cause resentment if works staff look upon the surveyor as a policeman. Eric avoided this pitfall. He discussed his findings and recommendations as he went along with individual plant managers. His reports were then issued in draft. By the time the works manager and production director saw the final reports, the actions were agreed and often completed. Works staff accepted Eric as someone who could help them by drawing their attention to hazards they were not aware of, as a result of ignorance, lack of time for detailed investigations or because we all fail to notice what we see every day.

Following the Nylon Works fire I recruited a second surveyor and the Wilton site safety manager recruited two auditors. Gradually, over the next 13 years the size of the auditing team was reduced, as standards improved, but it went too far and by the time I retired in 1982 there were, as we shall see, none at all.

The team grows
Eric Hunt was not my first recruit. In 1968 the Factory Inspectorate issued a draft of a proposed new Factories Act. It was longer and more complex than the 1961 Act and clearly required careful study. At the suggestion of one of the works managers, Ken Gee gave me a senior member of Technical Department, Sydney Lamb, as an assistant. His main job was be the detailed consideration of the proposals and the submission of comments. He stayed with me until he retired about five years later. He took the case history discussions when I was not available and carried out a number of other jobs.

So many objections were raised to the mass of detailed rules in the draft Factories Act that the government set up a committee to consider the future of health and safety legislation. It was chaired by Lord Robens and they spent a day at Wilton. Their report led to the 1974 Health and Safety at Work Act and an entirely new legislative approach, goal-based rather than rule-based. Instead of a "telephone directory" of detailed regulations, there is now a general requirement to provide a safe plant and system of work and adequate instruction, training and supervision. In the first place it is up to the employer to decide what is a safe plant etc, but if the Health and Safety Executive inspector does not agree he can say so and, if necessary, issue Improvement or Prohibition Notices.

Henry Simpson arrives

Before I took up the safety appointment, Henry Simpson had moved to Technical Department where he investigated a number of safety problems in depth, particularly the design of equipment for handling liquefied flammable gases. This was a direct result of the propane fire at Feyzin, France, in 1966 that killed 18 people and injured many more. Henry's report was a masterly summary of the design requirements, which I still quote. I have visited modern plants that do not have the safety features he recommended over thirty years ago.

I co-operated closely with Henry and when he retired in 1971 he was retained part-time as a member of my team, now called Safety and Loss Prevention Group. His successor, Alan Pugh, was also transferred to my Group, so there were now five and a half of us, plus a very competent secretary.

Henry Simpson, incidentally, was a good example of an "autumn flower", a man who does his best work late in his career. (I suppose I am also one.) There is a tendency in industry and the media to be in awe of the high-flyer who shows promise early and is quickly promoted. The autumn flowers can contribute as much, sometimes when the spring flowers have faded.

How I spent my time

Though my team grew I never spent more than about a quarter of my time on managerial duties. They were all men of experience and ability who could be left to get on with their own jobs. I was a "working leading-hand", allocating the work, keeping a general eye on it, available to advise if necessary, but spending most of my time doing my share of the work of the Group.

As a section manager and assistant works manager, though responsible for the operation of the section or works, most of my time was spent on non-technical duties — labour relations, production scheduling, costs, liaison with other departments, plant tidiness and everyday safety — and technical problems took up only a small part of the day. When I became safety adviser, I wondered how I would take to a return to full-time technical work. Most people do less and less as they get older. I found I loved it, and never regretted the move. On Monday mornings when the alarm clock rang, I used to look forward to the whole week in front of me. Of course, it was not just the interest of the job, but the fact that I was left in peace to do what I thought right that contributed to my job satisfaction.

An advantage of being an "expert"
At first I continued to advocate the same views as I had advocated on Oil Works. But I was now officially the expert and some people took much more notice, sometimes taking out their notebooks and writing down what I said.

On the whole though I had to manage by persuasion, not authority. In some ways it can be easier. These days our subordinates take little notice of an instruction if they are not convinced it is the right thing to do. We have to be persuasive in any case. If you do not have direct authority you cannot be tempted to use it. However, once you become recognised as an expert, you may find that your tentative proposals become carved in tablets of stone.

In his biography of the photographer Robert Capa, Richard Whelan relates how an unknown young photographer in Paris, André Freedmann, had difficulty selling his work. His girl friend posed as the agent for a "fabulously successful" American, Robert Capa, and sold his photos for three times the going rate (Whelan R, *Biography of Robert Capa*, Faber & Faber, London, 1985).

The works safety officers remained members of the works staff. But they were mainly non-technical. Excellent experienced men as they were, by background and training they tended, with one or two exceptions, not to be interested in the measures I was advocating. Though I spoke to individual managers on the works, I had no central point of contact, no individual who could pick up my ideas and run with them. The works managers recognised this and one by one appointed experienced plant managers as full-time "technical safety managers", usually retaining a non-technical safety officer or a safety foreman to assist each one.

Hazop revived

The next recruit to the Group was Bert Lawley, a former colleague from Oil Works Process Investigation Section and at the time the Division's expert on Hazop studies, described in Chapter 5. He had belonged to Management Services Department (MSD). When MSD was abolished (see page 68) Bert was first transferred to the Central Investigation Department, which did not understand his work and was not interested in it. It looked as if Hazop could lapse, not because anyone had taken a considered decision to scrap it but as a side-effect of the disappearance of MSD, throwing out the baby with the bathwater. I went round lobbying various people and in the end Bert was transferred to my Group, where he flourished. When he became responsible for leading Hazop studies, they were rather run down. Bert revived them, developed them, applied them to many projects, taught the technique to many others and became widely recognised as one of its foremost exponents. His 1973 paper, the first published paper on Hazop, has been widely quoted and has become a classic (Lawley H G, *Chemical Engineering Progress*, Vol 70, No 4, 1974, p45).

Another reorganisation

In 1971 a major shake-up of the ICI Divisions was announced. The three Nylon Works (at Wilton, Billingham and Ardeer, in Scotland, but the Billingham Works was soon closed) and Davies Works at Wilton, part of Fibres Division, which manufactured terephthalic acid, the monomer from which polyester fibre is made, were transferred to HOC Division, now renamed Petrochemicals Division. The size of my parish was roughly doubled and now included most of the Wilton site. However, before I could get to grips with the new problems, I was removed from the safety scene for a few months.

8

JOB ASSESSMENT

All organisations have job descriptions written for the purpose of fixing the correct rate of pay for the job but these are not intended to define what you may and may not do. They tell you what the people who wrote them did, not what their successors can and cannot do.

From an ICI note on job assessment.

All large organisations have schemes for assessing the rates of pay for different jobs. Marks are awarded under various headings such as skill and knowledge, management skills and responsibility and are then combined to arrive at an overall rating for the job. The emphasis is on the job, rather than the individual performance, but there is usually some way of rewarding above-average performance.

The ICI system for monthly-paid employees was considered adequate for line jobs. However, it did not adequately reward people who held advisory appointments. To get good people to accept and remain in such appointments, various fiddles had to be worked. People moved to an advisory job kept their rates of pay as personal allowances if they had proved their worth at their level. They got cost-of-living rises but nothing more, though exceptionally a case could be made for an extra 5 or even 10%.

London acts on job assessment

The Central Personnel Department (CPD) in London decided to set up a committee to consider the future of job assessment for monthly paid staff. A newly-appointed "new ideas" man in CPD set about his task with great enthusiasm and even greater expenditure of other people's time, recruiting staff from the Divisions that would co-operate onto various committees. I was picked to head one on job assessment.

The first I heard about it was a 'phone call from the acting personnel director telling me I had to drop everything else for three months. No questions about what would be involved, the effect on other work, just "get on with it". It showed how shallow was the effect of all the management training over the years on the need to sell ideas to people, to get them involved and so on. Perhaps not very wisely, I made my views known, went off to a conference in Holland for a week (CPD thought I ought to start the new job the same day), tidied up outstanding work and tried to find out something about job assessment.

I had an assistant and a steering committee of four people from other Divisions. My assistant and I were to visit various sites to find out what people thought was wrong with the existing system and then to write a report for consideration by the committee.

This was a bad system as the committee had not been exposed to the sites' views and could not therefore fully appreciate the reasons for our conclusions. It took many meetings to hammer out an agreed view, but we did so in the end.

Walking the tightrope

I put my foot in it in the first week. Our remit said that we were to ascertain the views of managers and staff. Starting on my home ground, I organised a series of meetings with a cross-section of staff to get their views. CPD rang up in a flap. "We did not expect you to talk to staff. There are other ways of finding out their views. There is a strong feeling in the Divisions that staff ought not to be involved; that it should just be a management exercise. You may have lost the confidence of the Divisions." However, in the end it was agreed that we could talk to

Division staff provided the management of that Division agreed: most did; a few did not.

Our report recommended a basic change to the assessment system. For each heading under which marks are awarded we proposed two sets of descriptions: the existing ones for use with line jobs and a new set for use with advisory jobs.

After three months I went back to my normal duties. A few months later I attended a meeting of Division personnel directors to discuss my report. There was a long agenda and it was obvious from the comments that many of the directors had not read the report. Nevertheless our recommendations were adopted and another committee was set up to consider them in greater detail.

The dust settles

The new scheme did not produce the results we hoped for. Advisors (and their managers) continued to feel that they were poorly rewarded compared with line staff. I had long unsuccessful struggles to try and get what I thought were the right rates of pay for the members of my Group. In practice, advisory jobs continued to be filled by horizontal transfer from a line job and the adviser took his rank with him as a personal allowance, even though it was well above the official rating of the new job. This meant that only people who did not expect to be promoted any further could fill advisory jobs. It was still possible to get them an extra 5 or 10% as an extra personal allowance but that was all.

9

SAFETY ADVISER — PART 2

There is a tide in the affairs of men,
Which, taken at the flood, leads on to fortune;
Omitted, all the voyage of their life
Is bound in shallows and miseries.
On such a full sea are we now afloat:
And we must take the current when it serves,
Or lose our ventures.

Shakespeare, Julius Caesar, Act 4, Scene 3

I am not sure about the fortune but I did try, during my time as a safety adviser, to take advantage of the opportunities that, by being at the right place at the right time, had fallen my way.

Conferences on loss prevention

I returned to my safety duties in time to attend a major conference in July 1971, the first of many that I was to attend in the coming years. The conference, on Loss Prevention in the Process Industries, was held in Newcastle and organised by the Institution of Chemical Engineers. It was the first of a series of three-yearly European conferences on the subject. The idea came from my colleague Ted Kantyka who was also responsible for many of the other initiatives in loss prevention that the Institution of Chemical Engineers took during the 1970s. Safety was not one of his responsibilities, except insofar as it is every manager's responsibility, but he saw its growing importance and persuaded the Institution that they should sponsor conferences and publications in this field. Fortunately I had prepared my paper for the conference in good time.

One of the papers presented at the conference was a now classical paper by N A R Bell on the manufacture of nitroglycerine (*Loss Prevention in the Process Industries*, Symposium Series No 34, Institution of Chemical Engineers, Rugby, 1971, p50). In the old method, illustrated in Figure 3.3, page 31, acid and glycerine were mixed in a large stirred reactor holding about a ton of raw materials and product watched over, readers will recall, by an operator sitting on a one-legged stool. If the temperature got too hot the reactor exploded, taking the operator with it. The reactor was so large because the reaction was slow. But it was not really slow. Once the molecules came together they reacted quickly. The reaction appeared to be slow because the mixing was poor. Once this was realised it became possible to design a small, well-mixed reactor with the same output as the old one but containing only about a kilogram. The new reactor resembled a laboratory water pump. A stream of acid sucked in the glycerine through a side arm and by the time the mixture left the reactor the reaction was complete. The residence time fell from an hour to a couple of minutes. The maximum size of an explosion was greatly reduced, not by adding on protective equipment that might fail or be neglected but by the inherent or intrinsic nature of the process: what you don't have, can't explode. I was later to quote this paper as an excellent example of inherently safer design — that is, designs that are safe because of their nature rather than made safe by adding on layers of protection.

Learning from the USA

Also in 1971 I went to the annual Loss Prevention Symposium organised by the American Institute of Chemical Engineers and attended almost every year until 1990. I found that in the USA technical people had been involved in safety and loss prevention for many years. I had a lot to learn from them and made many friends.

I acquired over the years a reputation as a frequent conference-goer. Ron Thomson, production manager from about 1970, used to say that fortunately I had to come back to collect my expenses or they would never see me. But reality in the safety and loss prevention field makes it necessary to keep in touch with developments elsewhere and, equally important, to tell other people what you are doing. I rarely, if ever, went to conferences without presenting a paper and by the time I retired had published over 80 (though not all presented at conferences).

The conferences I attended, both internal-ICI and external, were technical ones. I soon found that conferences on traditional approaches to safety were dull and uninspiring and gave up attending the regular meetings of ICI Division safety advisers.

Newcomers to Petrochemicals Division

When I returned to full-time safety work, much of my time was taken up with the extension of our activities to the three new works that had joined the Division — the Nylon Works at Wilton and Ardeer (in Ayrshire) and the terephthalic acid works (known as Davies Works) at Wilton. The Billingham Nylon Works, as already mentioned, was soon closed to reduce excess production capacity. These works made monomers only. Polymerisation and spinning continued to be the responsibility of other Divisions.

When a works was transferred from one Division to another, ICI's method — never written down anywhere but part of the culture — was to bring it into line with the ways of the new Division very gently and gradually. It was rather like the way of the Inca emperors (Wilson S M, *Natural History*, April 1991, p22):

> They also carried off the leading chief and all his children to Cuzco, where they were treated with kindness and favor so that by frequenting the court they would learn not only its laws, customs and correct speech, but also the rites, ceremonies and superstitions of the Incas. This done the chief was restored to his former dignity and authority...

However, it was not always so. Sir John Harvey-Jones says that when HOC Division took over responsibility for the Wilton site in 1963 it was brash, aggressive and arrogant (*Getting it Together*, Heinemann, London,

1991, p276). Perhaps the production function was different. More likely, John, having seen the dark side of the 1963 merger, was able to influence the later one.

Though the two Nylon Works were very competently run — the Ardeer Works outstandingly so — their organisation was very different from that of Olefine and Oil Works. The job of these works was production only. The other works carried out their own research, design, commercial activities and so on. Gradually these extraneous activities were moved to the Petrochemicals HQ departments. The Nylon Works were also rather more generously staffed than the old HOC Division works; the numbers were gradually reduced. Nylon was less profitable than in the past and its licence to print money was over.

Terephthalic mavericks

From the point of view of my Group, we had to bring the new works into our auditing scheme, make them aware of our services, and so on. We already had good relations with the Nylon Works staff and there were no problems. Davies Works was a little more difficult. When I started looking round I found lots of things that horrified me: alarms and trips never tested and not working, equipment in operation although a permit-to-work for repairs had not been signed off. A manager actually said to me, "We can't wait until maintenance have time to sign them off. We've got to get the plant running". I asked an operator why an alarm light was showing on the panel and he said, "Buggered if I know". In HOC Division operators were usually able to explain the reasons for red lights.

I do not blame the staff. When we join an organisation most of us accept what we find as normal. "When in Rome do as Rome does". It is only the exceptional person, or the one with experience of other ways, who is able to change things. The Division moved a number of ex-HOC people into Davies Works and gradually it was brought up to scratch.

After an accident managers are often criticised unfairly. They may never have worked anywhere else and may not realise that the standards they enforced were too low. Their training as students or in the company may not have covered permits-to-work or modification control procedures or the need to test alarms and trips. Today, in the UK, all chemical engineering undergraduates do get some training in safety and loss prevention, but it tends to be theoretical rather than practical.

Hazard analysis

I have come to be particularly associated with the subject of one of my first papers, presented at Newcastle in 1971, the application of numerical methods to safety problems. There are never enough resources available to remove all hazards. How do we decide which to deal with first? Only, I suggested, by setting a target or criterion and removing or reducing those risks which exceed the target value. I had been applying these methods since 1968, they were catching on in the Division and in the company, and I was able to include in my paper many examples to show how hazard analysis, as I called it, had helped us solve priority problems.

I intended at first to use the term "risk analysis" but then realised that this was used in ICI to describe a method for estimating the commercial risks of a project, so I used "hazard analysis" (sometimes abbreviated to Hazan) instead. Today it is better known as quantitative risk assessment (QRA).

I start to publish papers

Ken Gee had at first been hesitant about allowing me to publish a paper which implied that we set a target for risks to life and tolerated those risks which were below the target. At his suggestion I re-wrote my first draft with the emphasis on priorities rather than acceptance of risk, and this was approved by Edward Challis who succeeded Gee as Production Director.

Over the years the Division, in effect Edward Challis, allowed me to publish widely, far more widely than most other companies would have permitted. My first paper dealt with risks to employees but later I discussed risks to the public. A friend in Esso once said, "There is no way that Esso would have let me publish a paper which openly said that if a risk to the public is below a certain level, we should not spend scarce resources on reducing it further".

Since 1971 I have published other papers on hazard analysis and, after retiring from ICI, a book called *Hazop and Hazan — Identifying and Assessing Process Industry Hazards*, now in its 4th edition (Institution of

Chemical Engineers, Rugby, 1999). I have lectured on this subject many times.

The appeal of hazard analysis

I found that colleagues in ICI took to hazard analysis because scientists and engineers like to solve problems numerically, when they can, rather than by gut feel. Objections to the use of the methods began to be raised only when risks to the public were discussed in this way and non-technical people became involved.

I do not want to give the impression that I invented hazard analysis. It was applied in the nuclear industry by Reg Farmer and others before I came on the scene and within ICI my colleague Mike Stewart applied it to a specific problem — the design of a protective system for a new ethylene oxide plant. Independently he and I arrived at much the same criteria.

Bert Lawley, as well as being a superb practitioner of Hazop (see pp89-90), also became very skilled in hazard analysis. His published papers on the subject are little masterpieces, the reasons for each figure and each step being set out in comprehensive detail.

Insurance

About this time I got involved with the company's captive insurance company, Imperial Chemicals Insurance. As a result of the Polythene Plant explosion and Nylon Works fire (see Chapter 7) ICI got back from the insurance companies all the money they had paid in premiums since the end of the war, and more. Premiums rose steeply and it became necessary to see that they were allocated fairly between the Divisions and plants. When they were small it hardly mattered. The insurance company surveyors were men of great practical experience but were not able to assess technical risks. I helped IC Insurance to do so and kept in touch with the new-style surveyors they soon appointed.

Flixborough explodes

In 1974 a chemical plant at Flixborough on Humberside exploded, killing 28 men, and the world of process safety was never the same again. The number killed may not seem all that large compared with the numbers killed in plane and train crashes, dam collapses and road accidents but it was the worst chemical plant accident to have occurred in the UK, and one of the worst anywhere for several decades. It made the headlines in the press and there were many demands for greater control of the industry.

The government set up two committees, one to consider the immediate causes and the other to look at wider questions. Edward Challis was on the latter, the Advisory Committee on Major Hazards, and I was co-opted onto one of its Working Groups and attended occasional meetings of others. They worked slowly; their final report was not issued until 1984 and the changes in legislation they recommended in earlier reports took effect in the same year. The Health and Safety Executive now takes much interest in "major hazards", as they are called.

Though the law changed slowly, the impact on my work was immediate. The Flixborough explosion was the result of a plant modification and showed the need for greater control of them. We had already recognised this but Flixborough gave it added urgency and for a year my weekly safety discussions were devoted to this subject.

Inherently safer design

We also spent a lot of time considering the probabilities and effects of explosions and the conditions necessary for them to occur, the need for better plant layout and stronger control rooms and many other matters. At the 1975 American Institute of Chemical Engineers Loss Prevention Symposium I presented a paper on the wider questions raised by Flixborough. I pointed out that the leak was so large, about 50 tonnes, and the explosion so devastating because the conversion was only about 6% per pass. So most of the raw material had to be recovered and recycled many times.

The most effective way of reducing the size of any leak would be to improve the conversion and thus reduce the inventory in the plant. Whenever possible we should design our plants so that they do not contain large quantities of hazardous materials or use safer materials instead. I included some examples of what had been or might be done. Later I expanded this section of the paper into a lecture for the Society of Chemical Industry, entitled "What you don't have, can't leak" (*Chemistry and Industry*, 6 May 1978, p287). Over the years I continued to advocate these inherently safer plants, as they are called, and after retiring from ICI wrote a short book on the subject, now in its 4th edition and no longer short (*Process Plants: A Handbook for Inherently Safer Design*, 2nd edition, Taylor & Francis, Philadelphia, PA, 1998).

Developing inherently safer design

In the book and in my lectures I compared the old and new methods for the manufacture of nitroglycerine and suggested that similar changes should be possible in the chemical and oil industries. Within ICI Colin Ramshaw had shown that many unit operations could be intensified — that is, carried out with a much smaller inventory in the equipment — and that because the equipment is smaller it is usually cheaper. He later moved to Newcastle University to continue his work there.

The normal procedure in plant design is to:
- design a plant;
- identify the hazards (today using systematic techniques like Hazop);
- add on protective equipment to control the hazards.

Some hazards are obvious but many are not and are not identified until late in design. All we can do then is to *control* them by adding on gas detectors, trips, alarms, emergency valves, steam and water curtains, fire-proofing and so on or by relying on procedures. I had spent (by this time) ten years urging people to control hazards by adding on protective equipment before I realised that it would be better to remove the hazards, by intensification or in other ways, such as:
- substitution: using non-flammable and non-toxic materials instead of hazardous ones;
- attenuation: using hazardous materials in the least hazardous form, for example, explosive powders can be handled as slurries;
- limitation of effects by changing designs or reaction conditions rather than adding on control equipment. For example, it is better to prevent overheating by limiting the temperature of the heating medium than by relying on a high temperature trip.

The reader may feel that much of this is obvious and that no-one would include a large inventory of hazardous material in a design unless it was really necessary, but in fact most designers had given little or no thought to ways of reducing inventories. They just designed a plant and accepted whatever amount of material was called for by the design, confident of their ability to keep the hazards under control. Flixborough weakened the public's confidence in that ability and ten years later Bhopal (see Chapter 10) almost destroyed it.

Of lions and lambs

Two analogies may make what I am advocating a little clearer. If the meat of lions were good to eat, farmers would be asked to farm lions. They would need strong cages round their fields and only occasionally, as at Flixborough, would the lions escape. But why keep lions when lambs will do instead?

The stairs are the most dangerous piece of equipment in our homes. The traditional safety officer's approach is to urge people to use the banisters and keep the stairs free from tripping hazards. The inherently safer solution is to live in a bungalow. We can't fall down stairs that aren't there.

Keeping it simple

The book on inherently safer design also covers simplification. I was attending an ICI safety symposium at which someone described an explosion on a batch reactor. He showed a line diagram of the reactor before the explosion and then a line diagram of the modified reactor after the recommendations of the investigating team had been carried out. The reactor could hardly be seen for the mass of protective instruments added on. My neighbour and I looked at each other and both of us said, "That can't be right". Complexity is never desirable as it produces more equipment that can go wrong and more opportunities for human error. We are willing to pay more for complexity but not for simplicity.

My neighbour at the symposium was Derek Facey, the head of the Division's process design section — that is, he was responsible for the choice of process and the early stages of design and then passed on the flowsheets to the rest of the Engineering Department for detailed design. He made a real effort to encourage more critical study of designs at an early stage but after he left a lot of the momentum was lost.

Later I advocated other ways of making plants more user-friendly, such as:

- Making incorrect assembly impossible.
- Avoiding knock-on effects: for example, reducing the spread of fire by providing gaps between units, like the fire breaks in a forest.
- Making status clear: we should be able to see at a glance whether a valve is open or shut.
- Avoiding equipment, such as hoses and bellows, that is intolerant of misuse.

A slow fuse

Interest in inherently safer designs has grown gradually since 1974 but far more slowly than interest in Hazop and hazard analysis for a number of reasons, discussed in my book on inherently safer designs. One reason is that these designs require more time for the consideration of alternatives at the early stages of design. This time is rarely available because when the need for a new plant is recognised it is wanted as soon as possible. My former Oil Works colleague Bob (now Sir Robert) Malpas later suggested that while we are designing the next plant we should start thinking about the plant after next, for at that time we are conscious of all the changes we might make but do not have time to think through.

In addition, I sometimes feel there is a conceptual lock, a reluctance to adopt a new principle. Many people will adopt new gadgets and new techniques, such as Hazop, but changing the design process to incorporate a new philosophy is more difficult. Many engineers are more interested in the "How" than in questioning the "What". They buy more copies of my "How to" books than of my ideas books.

The Polytechnic course

In 1973 the staff of the Department of Chemical Engineering at Teesside Polytechnic (now University) suggested that we collaborate in the organisation of a one-week course in process safety for people from other industries and organisations. We agreed to take part and the course was scheduled for July 1974. As it turned out, this was a month after the explosion at Flixborough; the chemical industry suddenly became more conscious of the importance of safety and the 75 places were all filled. I and other members of the Safety and Loss Prevention Group presented well over half the course so it was really

Petrochemicals Division making its knowledge and experience in process safety available to the whole of the industry. The emphasis was on participation. The students were divided into groups of 12 to 25 and they discussed accidents that had happened, as already described, or they carried out hazard and operability studies.

The course was held each year and continued to be a sell-out until 1981 after which numbers fell. It ended in the mid-1980s. Today most courses are shorter as companies cannot spare people for a whole week.

Travel

During my first 25 years with ICI I never went abroad for the company. As safety adviser I soon made up for lost time, visiting ICI plants and other companies all over the globe. An overwhelming impression from these visits was of the uniformity of ICI. Wherever I went similar people tackled similar problems in similar ways. Only the accents were different. In India, a personnel officer interrupted my discussion with a works manager with an urgent problem arising out of a recent strike. The works manager dealt with it the same way as a works manager at Billingham or Wilton would have done. Most of ICI's senior overseas staff had worked in the UK and had also been exposed to ICI men seconded overseas. In this way ICI (like the Incas) found the true secret of empire: do not try to control by instructions, but by exposing people to your ways. If they are good, people will copy them.

I have also noticed, not just overseas but in the UK, that ICI and ex-ICI people have an affinity with each other or at least a sense of knowing how to deal with each other. They share, by and large, the same outlook and the same way of dealing with problems. Now that ICI has sold most of its plants, and the staff that go with them, and bought others in their place, this sense of commonality will have been lost.

The only exception to the ICI uniformity was ICI Americas. ICI bought Atlas and changed the name, but Atlas ways continued. Although some ICI people were seconded there they had difficulty persuading the Americans that ICI ways were any good.

More members of the Group

I started off in 1968 with a part-time secretary. I soon found the need for a full-time one and when the Group grew I was able to recruit a second.

It was my good fortune to have some very good secretaries and the best of them, Eileen Turner, who arrived just after Flixborough and stayed until 1980, was outstanding. She hesitated before accepting the job, as she feared that the pace in an advisory department in a large organisation might be rather undemanding. She need not have worried, as she admitted after a few months. She was surprised to find such a sense of urgency.

Many of our clients did want quick answers. But a lot of the pressure was self-generated. I thought of things we might do, decided to do them, and then wanted them done quickly. That was the way I tended to work and I think you get more done that way than dealing with each problem in its own good time. No group of employees shows more variation in ability than typists and secretaries. Many are more intelligent than their bosses, though they lack specialised knowledge. Many are under-used. I always tried to give my secretaries as much responsibility as they could take and in Eileen's case that was a lot.

Jim McQuaid

During 1976/7 Jim McQuaid was seconded to us for a year from the Research and Laboratory Services Division of the Health and Safety Executive (formerly the Safety in Mines Research Establishment). The move was of value to both sides. With his different background he was able to bring fresh insights to bear on some of our problems. For example, ICI had used steam curtains in a number of plants for confining and dispersing leaks. Other companies (and a few ICI plants) had used water curtains instead but no-one really knew how to design them; they simply sprayed a lot of water around and hoped it would be enough. Jim had been involved in the design of water barriers to prevent the spread of explosions in coal mines. This was a very different application but nevertheless gave him an understanding of water spray that enabled him to develop a design method for water curtains.

Jim, in exchange for the work he did for us, gained an inside view of industrial safety. He was a full member of the Group and had access to all our files. Ron Thomson once asked me if it were wise to ask him to look into a minor explosion, which reflected no great credit on those involved, and where the recommendations did not seem very far-reaching. In fact, Jim concluded that the works staff had over-reacted.

Jim returned to his old job when the year was over. He went on to become Director of the Research and Laboratory Services Division and later Director of HSE's Science and Technology Directorate.

Basil Eddershaw and others

Basil Eddershaw had shared the case history discussions with me since Sydney Lamb retired. A mechanical engineer by profession, he balanced the preponderance of chemists in the Group and was outstandingly good at all aspects of training. Ron Parvin joined the Group at about the same time. He was the only young (under 40) person I was able to recruit (secretaries excepted). He and Bert Lawley spent most of their time on hazard and operability studies and hazard analyses but could scarcely cope with the work load. A request for extra staff would not have been received sympathetically, to say the least, but there are ways round such difficulties.

When Management Services Department was annihilated (see page 68) a rump of the old work study function survived as the Productivity Services Section of Personnel Department. I suggested to the section head that he might take on some of the hazard and operability studies. He jumped at the chance as much of their work was pretty mundane. He was glad of something more challenging and allocated the two best members of his team, Ron Fawcett and Frank Mitchell, to the work. Later, when Productivity Services followed Management Services into oblivion, they were transferred to my Group.

Using the system

In large organisations it is little use grumbling because the organisation will not give you the resources you think you need. Instead of opposing the system, it is better to use it.

Here is an example: I had accumulated extensive files and knew my way about them. There was no indexing system but I could usually remember where I had put things. However, as it grew, the quantity of paper might overload my memory and I was not going to be around for ever.

I started to index our files on a computerised information storage and retrieval system, using a system that could be accessed by anyone in ICI. Many ICI information people were, rightly, more concerned with keeping information confidential than spreading it, but in safety as many people as possible need to know. (Accident reports, like farmyard muck, stink and should be spread.)

Progress was slow as it was a spare time job for Eileen Turner and me. It became clear I needed someone full-time on the job. At the time, about 1978, the pressure on numbers was intense. However, jobs were often combined or reduced a year or more before their occupants retired and they were available for that year. I was fortunate in being able to recruit an experienced safety adviser, Stanley Beaumont, a former Oil Works colleague, for a year to develop the use of the computerised storage system. When Stanley finally retired Ron Fawcett took over the work.

Computers and literature

The effort lapsed after I retired. By 1999 computerised storage and retrieval of information was widely used and someone asked what had happened to my old computer files. no-one could find them and if they found them it was doubtful if they would be able to open them. Only 10% of ancient Greek literature and a third of ancient Latin literature have survived to the present day. I wonder what the figure is for ancient (that is, pre-1985) computer files? We learn more quickly and forget sooner than earlier generations.

Another example of the way in which one can get round company rules comes from ICI's Central Personnel Department. Someone wanted to talk to the trades unions on a subject that officially should not be discussed. Ever helpful, the Department said that negotiations were not yet possible and even consultations would be unwise but there was no reason why there should not be an exchange of views. In large organisations it is easier to interpret the rules flexibly to meet changed circumstances than to change them.

Harland Frank and other colleagues

A colleague with whom I collaborated closely at this time was Harland Frank, the best engineer I ever knew. About my age, he served his time as an apprentice in a firm of marine engineers, was released to take a degree in mechanical engineering, was in the Army during the war and joined ICI after demobilisation.

I first met him in 1959 when we sat at the same table in the canteen; we had regular seats then. I was just married, was busy with do-it-yourself jobs and found him a useful source of information on the right tools, materials and methods; he could tackle anything. He held various jobs in design and maintenance and by the time I became safety adviser he was works engineer at North Tees. He had a heart attack but seemed to get over it and about 1970 was appointed production engineering adviser, with a remit somewhat parallel to my own, advising the works on engineering standards and methods and trying by persuasion, not authority, to ensure a uniformity of good practice. He was, like me, responsible to the production director, and moved into the next office.

With Ron Thomson, the production manager, and Barry Whitefoot, the environmental adviser, we formed a quartet of satellites in orbit round the production director, though I was the only one with supporting staff. Harland returned to Engineering Department for a couple of years but following a serious operation he returned to his old job as engineering adviser. He was a skilled craftsman, had an encyclopaedic knowledge of practical engineering and knew his theory, so he was a mine of information on all engineering matters. He was also very willing to spread his knowledge. I discussed the engineering aspects of my problems with him and benefited enormously. He was a doer and a talker rather than a writer but did put some of his knowledge down on paper in various memoranda. At one time he produced an occasional newsletter, *The Terotechnologist*, and later contributed a page to my monthly *Safety Newsletter*.

He retired early about the end of 1980 and, sadly, died a year later. I was then only a few months from my own retirement but I now wish that I had, during this period, collected together his various notes and issued them as an ICI Report. It would have helped to preserve them. Any young engineer who can locate and copy his writings will have acquired a bag of gold.

I also saw a lot of Barry Whitefoot, the environmental adviser and for a time toxicological adviser as well. While I was interested in hazards that could kill or injure people quickly he was concerned only with those that had long, slow, lingering effects — rather odd perhaps for such a kindly man. He was one of the most helpful men I have ever known and his judgement was sound. He was ideally suited to his job.

During my time in ICI there was never a shortage of expert advice. There were colleagues who were expert in everything connected with the manufacture of chemicals. The only problem was finding out who they were. Occasionally someone kept up his expertise as a hobby after moving to another department. Bill High, an engineer on Oil Works, was an expert on explosions and almost a part-time unpaid member of my Group.

Safety Newsletter

I have already mentioned my monthly *Safety Newsletter*. In 1968 I sent copies of No 1 to about 30 colleagues, mainly those working in the safety field. The *Newsletter* contained various bits and pieces of information that I thought would interest them. Gradually, over the next 14 years, the circulation and contents grew. The circulation grew spontaneously; I did not advertise it, but added people to the list at their request. By the time I retired, the circulation was several thousand, including all ICI Divisions, many outside companies, universities and the Health and Safety Executive.

Within ICI it was seen by directors, managers, foremen and, in some works, operators. Some other companies photocopied it and distributed it widely. The contents came to consist mainly of reports on accidents of general and technical interest from ICI and from other companies, supplied in exchange for the *Newsletter*. I did not copy the original reports, but rewrote them to bring out the essential messages. Many later *Newsletters* were devoted to specific themes, such as accidents due to plant modifications, preparation for maintenance, static electricity, human error.

After I retired I edited many items from old *Newsletters* and published them in a book called *What Went Wrong?* Now in its 4th edition, and my best-selling book, I have added many later reports (*What Went Wrong? — Case Histories of Process Plant Disasters*, 4th edition, Gulf, Houston, Texas, 1998).

ICI's attitude to disclosure

Why was ICI so willing to let me send reports of our errors all over the world? Well, I never asked permission, and if I had it might have been refused. The circulation, as I have said, just grew. But Edward Challis and the Division Board were very supportive. We felt it right to spread information, for several reasons:

1. Moral — if we have information which may prevent accidents there is a moral duty to pass it on to other people.
2. Economic — ICI spent a lot of money on safety. By telling our competitors what we did we encouraged them to spend as much.
3. Pragmatic — we got useful information from other companies in return.
4. In the eyes of the public, the chemical industry is one. The whole industry suffers if one company performs badly. The explosion at Flixborough in 1974, which killed 28 people (see page 99), not only gave the industry a poor reputation but resulted in the whole industry having to take additional precautions which in some cases may have perhaps gone further than was really necessary. The effects of the leaks at Seveso, Italy in 1976, which killed no-one, were even more marked in this respect.

To misquote the well-known words of John Donne:

> No plant is an Island, entire of itself; every plant is a piece of the Continent, a part of the main. Any plant's loss diminishes us, because we are involved in the Industry: and therefore never send to know for whom the inquiry sitteth; it sitteth for thee.

The secret of describing accidents

Managers were willing to let me describe their accidents, which usually reflected no credit on them, because I did not say where they occurred. ICI in general, and Petrochemicals Division in particular, had a good reputation for reporting and investigating dangerous occurrences which did not cause injury, as well as those that did. Much can be learnt from these "near misses" but in many companies they are hushed up. Of course, I listened to lunch-time gossip and so on, and if I knew of an incident which had not been reported I went down to the works to see what I could find out. Some of the incidents in the *Newsletter* came to light in this way.

The *Newsletter* was not the only way in which I spread information on accidents and good practice. As already mentioned, I wrote many papers for journals and magazines, spoke at conferences and lectured to societies and other companies. My published work had to go through the company approval procedure but there were never any problems. Edward Challis did once query whether I was saying the same thing too often in different words, but if you are an evangelist for your ideas, as I was, it is necessary to do this. Giving the message once is never enough.

Occasionally I included a light-hearted item in the *Newsletter*. One such item, on a new fire-fighting agent, WATER, achieved a wider distribution than everything else I have written added together. It was reproduced by the Royal Society for the Prevention of Accidents in their magazine, noticed by the Chairman of Hoechst UK, quoted by him in a speech and reproduced by the *Sunday Times*. From there it was copied by numerous journals all over the world. I reproduce it on the following page. The article was translated into French as EAU *(Element Anti-feu Universel)*.

After I retired the *Safety Newsletter* continued for 18 months but then lapsed.

Safety discussions

The case history discussions described in Chapter 7 continued throughout my time as safety adviser, Basil Eddershaw sharing them with me and continuing them after my retirement. A list of some of the topics discussed shows the range of our interests:

- *Accidents due to human error:* our theme was that it is difficult to prevent these errors and so we should try to remove opportunities for error by changing the work situation — that is, the plant design or method of operation. After retiring from ICI I wrote a book on this topic, *An Engineer's View of Human Error*, now in its third edition (Institution of Chemical Engineers, Rugby, UK, 2000).
- *Organisations have no memory:* major accidents repeat themselves after ten or more years, as people leave and the lessons of the past are forgotten. How can we give organisations a memory? This was also expanded into a book (*Lessons from Disaster — How Organisations have No Memory and Accidents Recur*, Institution of Chemical Engineers, Rugby, 1993).
- *Accidents due to the over-pressuring of vessels:* this had been the cause

NEW FIRE-FIGHTING AGENT MEETS OPPOSITION "COULD KILL MEN AS WELL AS FIRES"

ICI has announced the discovery of a new fire-fighting agent to add to their existing range. Known as WATER (Wonderful And Total Extinguishing Resource), it augments, rather than replaces, existing agents such as dry powder and Halon which have been in use from time immemorial. It is particularly suitable for dealing with fires in buildings, timber yards and warehouses. Though required in large quantities, it is fairly cheap to produce and it is intended that quantities of about a million gallons should be stored in urban areas and near other installations of high risk ready for immediate use. Halon and dry powder are usually stored under pressure, but WATER will be stored in open ponds or reservoirs and conveyed to the scene of the fire by hoses and portable pumps.

ICI's new proposals are already encountering strong opposition from safety and environmental groups Professor Connie Barrinner has pointed out that if anyone immersed their head in a bucket of WATER, it would prove fatal in as little as 3 minutes. Each of ICI's proposed reservoirs will contain enough WATER to fill half a million two-gallon buckets. Each bucket-full could be used a hundred times so there is enough WATER in one reservoir to kill the entire population of the UK. Risks of this size, said Professor Barrinner, should not be allowed, whatever the gain. If the WATER were to get out of control the results of Flixborough or Seveso would pale into insignificance by comparison. What use was a fire-fighting agent that could kill men as well as fires?

A Local Authority spokesman said that he would strongly oppose planning permission for construction of a WATER reservoir in his area unless the most stringent precautions were followed. Open ponds were certainly not acceptable. What would prevent people falling in them? What would prevent the contents from leaking out? At the very least the WATER would need to be contained in a steel pressure vessel surrounded by a leak-proof concrete wall.

A spokesman from the Fire Brigades said he did not see the need for the new agent. Dry powder and Halon could cope with most fires. The new agent would bring with it risks, particularly to firemen, greater than any possible gain. Did we know what would happen to this new medium when it was exposed to intense heat? It had been reported that WATER was a constituent of beer. Did this mean that firemen would be intoxicated by the fumes?

The Friends of the World said that they had obtained a sample of WATER and found it caused clothes to shrink. If it did this to cotton, what would it do to men?

In the House of Commons yesterday, the Home Secretary was asked if he would prohibit the manufacture and storage of this lethal new material. The Home Secretary replied that, as it was clearly a major hazard, Local Authorities would have to take advice from the Health and Safety Executive before giving planning permission. A full investigation was needed and the Major Hazards Group would be asked to report.

of several serious incidents and this was the first module to be made available to the Institution of Chemical Engineers for them to sell.

- *Accidents due to instrument failure.*
- *Furnace fires and explosions.*
- *Accidents due to plant modifications.*
- *The lessons of Flixborough.*
- *Inherently safer and simpler plants* (see page 100).
- *Three weeks in a works:* all the incidents, big and little, that occurred in a three-week period (see *Learning from Accidents,* 2nd edition, Butterworth-Heinemann, Oxford, 1994, Chapter 15).
- *The lessons of Three-Mile Island.*

I put a lot of effort into these discussions but I also benefited from them as I was able to tap the accumulated wisdom and experience of those who attended. Many of the comments made in my papers and books are based on remarks made at these discussions.

Career development

My move to safety in 1968 had been a horizontal one. In 1970 I was moved up one step but soon afterwards assistant works managers were regraded and also moved up. At my annual performance reviews with Edward Challis I used to suggest that my reputation in the safety field justified an increase in grade but as I have indicated in Chapter 8 it is not easy for people in advisory jobs to move up. However in 1976 it happened. ICI had a system called the scientific ladder by which research workers could be rewarded outside the normal job assessment schemes. Those on the top grade received a salary similar to that of a senior university professor. In 1976 the rules were changed so that people in departments other than research could be eligible and I was the first person to be elected under the new regime.

Throughout my career I never looked further ahead than the next step, sometimes not even that far, and concentrated on doing my current job as well as I could. Some people say that one should set oneself a target at the start of one's career but this can lead to disappointment and frustration if one fails to get there. These planned careers have been satirised by Gilbert Adair (*Alice through the Needle's Eye,* Pan Books, London, 1985, p67):

> ...I decided — oh, many, many years ago — to write the story of my life, in advance, so that I could live it out afterwards. This way, I am sure to remember. Of course, it's not always easy to make everything work out, and it sometimes happens that I fall a little behind in my timetable.

I chose the quotation from Kafka for the beginning of this book (page ix) because like him I did not know where I was going. Some people are more like Homer's Odysseus; they have an aim in view, but they get distracted on the way.

The Loughborough proposal

In 1978 I was invited to become an industrial (that is a visiting) professor at Loughborough University of Technology. Professor Frank Lees, formerly of ICI Mond Division, had built up a team and reputation there in loss prevention and it was an honour to be invited to join them. The company readily agreed that I could spend an average of about one day per fortnight at the university. To reduce my workload Edward Challis transferred the two safety surveyors to the jurisdiction of the Wilton Site safety adviser. In retrospect, this was a mistake as it resulted in a rundown of the surveying effort.

Although I had been trained as a chemist, from my first move to the works in 1952 I had been doing jobs for which chemical engineering would have been a better training. I gradually found that chemistry journals no longer interested me, but chemical engineering ones did. I was involved with many of the loss prevention activities of the Institution of Chemical Engineers and a colleague suggested I join. I thought it would be a formality but it was not. It took them a year to consider my published work and agree that it could be accepted in lieu of a qualification in chemical engineering for election as a Member. Two years later I became a Fellow.

One of the Institution's initiatives in safety, another of Ted Kantyka's ideas, was the International Study Group on Hydrocarbon Oxidation (ISGHO). Set up after the Flixborough explosion, it was a club of companies operating similar processes. We met about twice a year to exchange information on a confidential basis. I was the first chairman, a member until I retired and was then invited to attend as a visitor for another few years. ISGHO was a most valuable source of information as companies were much more willing to describe their blunders there than in open meetings. The organisation still exists but has widened its remit and is now the International Process Safety Group.

Whispers about Hazop

An incident that occurred about 1979 illustrates an occasional feature of life in large organisations. I became aware that comments were being made at a senior level that hazard and operability studies (Hazops, see Chapter 5) were producing large unforeseen increases in the costs of new plants. People were asking, "Are the studies worthwhile? Should we scrap them?" There was no clearly articulated view, summarised in a memorandum, which one could counter, just rumours of what some-one was believed to have said. The words "whispering campaign" were used, but they imply a degree of deliberation that was probably not there. Instead one or two senior managers had a vague feeling of unease that something was wrong and they brought it up when triggered by a discussion. Edward Challis advised me that I had to take the allegations seriously.

If a plant has been badly designed, Hazop will bring this out. The design will have to be changed and this will probably increase the cost. The case against Hazop is thus the same as the case against visiting the doctor: he may recommend expensive or unpleasant treatment. But we do not have to accept the doctor's advice if we think the remedy is worse than the disease. In the same way we can accept a hazard in plant design if the results will be trivial or unlikely and the remedy is very expensive. In the words of the law, we are asked to do only what is "reasonably practicable", weighing in the balance the size of the risk and the cost, in money, time and trouble, of removing it. Note that there has to be a gross disproportion between them, the risk being insignificant compared with the cost. Note also that lack of resources is not a reason for accepting a risk and that it is wrong to stop looking for hazards in case we do not like what we find.

Hazoping the whispers

I talked to some of the project engineers. No, they said, on their plants Hazop had not caused unnecessary or unreasonable increases in cost and they were in favour of the studies, but they had heard it had done so elsewhere. I should talk to Tom. He said much the same and put me onto Dick who referred me to Harry. It was like looking for Russians with snow on their boots. no-one had seen them but everyone had heard of someone who had.

Finally, I wrote a note summarising my findings and had a talk with the engineering director. He said that when he (and others) commented on Hazop they not using the word in the precise sense in which I used it to describe a specific technique; they were using it as a generic term to describe the numerous studies carried out during the development of a design.

These, apart from Hazop, were mainly internal Engineering Department efforts. The anti-Hazop talk petered out.

Recession and retirement

In 1980 I began to think about retirement. Edward Challis and Ron Thomson, both younger than me, had retired. The company was offering very generous terms to anyone who would retire early, so that anyone staying on after the age of 57, my age at the beginning of the year, was working for very little more money than he would have got if he retired. We may have continued to work for pleasure, or out of habit or to occupy the time but certainly not for money.

I told Bob Clark, Edward's successor, that I was thinking of going in March 1982. For taxation reasons it was advisable to retire at the end of a financial year.

Then the recession hit the company. We had had periods of recession ever since I joined the company; they got greater and more frequent as the years went by, but the 1980 recession was the worst of the lot. It led to increased pressure on numbers and I had to see all my staff who were over 50 or approaching that dangerous age and advise them "to consider the advantages of early retirement", ICI's euphemism for "Get lost".

As it turned out, for all of them (and me) this was the best advice we ever received. One of them got an offer from another company at nearly twice the salary ICI was giving him. Another joined a consulting company that guaranteed him 25% employment but he ended up working full-time, and taking little time off for holidays. The third joined the same consultancy but made it clear that he wanted to work only two-thirds of the time. "No work from Wimbledon to the end of the Scarborough Cricket Festival" was his slogan. The fourth of the over-fifties stayed on and provided much needed continuity. I wondered if I ought to retire in 1981 but Bob Clark said it would be too soon for him to make adequate succession plans. During my last year I was the old-est person in the building.

In 1981 Petrochemicals and Plastics Divisions were merged to form a new Petrochemicals and Plastics Division but it took some time for the individual departments to be combined and, so far as loss prevention was concerned, this job was left to my successor.

The media catch up with me

In September 1981 I was asked to present a paper to the British Association meeting in York. Something fairly popular was wanted so I presented some information on risk in ways that the public might be able to understand. The usual ways of presenting risk such as 10^{-5} per person per year are incomprehensible to the layman and even a scien-tist finds it difficult to get a picture.

One of the suggestions, originally put forward by Harvard professor Richard Wilson, was to imagine a tax on risks. Everyone who creates a risk pays a tax proportional to the size of the risk. Let us assume that the basic rate is a million pounds per life, like all taxes an arbitrary figure.

Here are some of the taxes that we would have to pay (based on 1981 risk levels):

- Cigarettes   70p each
- Wine   £2 per bottle
- Beer   25p per pint
- Petrol   50p per gallon if used in a car
                                      £3 per gallon used in a motor cycle
- Chest X-ray   50p each
- Working in the chemical industry   £1.60 per week
- Working as a construction erector   £27 per week

I thought the paper was a fairly lightweight effort. But ICI put out a press release and it appealed to the media. It was summarised, on the whole quite fairly, in nearly all the daily papers and in many overseas ones and mentioned on the 10 o'clock ITV news. It led to interviews on local radio, an invitation to take part in a Radio 4 discussion and an appearance on local TV, my brief hour of glory.

Nearly 20 years later, while I was working on this book, the BBC telephoned. They were preparing a programme on risk and had heard that I had proposed a tax on risk. Could I tell them more about it?

Final days at ICI

In October 1981 I handed over to my successor, Alan Rimmer, moved into a smaller office and remained in a consultative capacity. However I found it hard to withdraw from the scene. I could have disappeared at Christmas, as many other retirees did, as I was entitled to five weeks holiday in 1982 plus another seven that I had banked ready for a sabbatical that I never took. However I chose to forgo my holiday and work right up to the end. I was not paid anything extra but on the other hand I spent two weeks in Japan on a lecture and consultancy tour, and some time preparing for my new job.

When Frank Lees at Loughborough heard that I was retiring he invited me to join the University for four days a week for three years and he was able to get a grant from the Science and Engineering Research Council to pay me a modest salary.

As my retirement present from the company I chose a filing cabinet instead of the cameras, fishing rods, boxes of records or other leisure goods chosen by my contemporaries. At the presentation Bob Clark remarked that ICI had not only supplied the cabinet but the paper to fill it. The company agreed I could write up for publication the material in *Safety Newsletters* and I was allowed to keep an office in the building and come in when I wanted to consult my old files. In exchange people could pick my brains. It was a very civilised arrangement (but see Chapter 10).

On 31 March 1982, my last day, nearly 38 years after I started, I was still in the office in the morning, dictating letters. I left at 12.00 noon to drive to Edinburgh to take part in a conference the next day, thus demonstrating that it was to be redeployment, not retirement.

I had spent the whole of my career in the Teesside area. In Agricultural and Petrochemicals Divisions this was quite common, as most of their plants were on Teesside. Colleagues in more scattered Divisions moved many times and seemed to live out of suitcases.

Retrospect

Figure 9.1 shows how ICI's fatal accidents rate fell during my 14 years in loss prevention. It reflects, I like to think, my impact on the job. Of course, many other people were working towards the same end and the graph does not prove that I achieved anything. But if the graph had remained level it would have shown that I had achieved nothing.

By the time I left the attitude to safety in the Division (and to a lesser extent in the company) had changed. It was no longer just a tiresome necessity but a technically interesting part of many people's jobs, whether they were in design, operations, maintenance or other functions. It was gratifying to feel that I had done something towards this change of attitude.

My approach, as the reader will have gathered, had been "technology driven" and "incident driven". I looked for the technical causes of incidents and tried to give my colleagues the technical information they

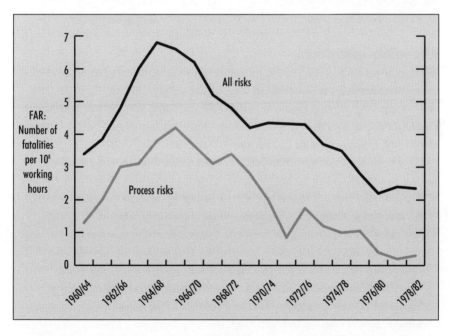

Figure 9.1: ICI's fatal accident rates (FAR — the number of fatal accidents in 10^8 working hours or in a group of 1000 men in a working lifetime) expressed as a five-year moving average

needed to prevent them happening again. I had little use for generalised exhortations to work safely.

People sometimes said, and still do, "We have done all we can to improve equipment. From now on we should concentrate on changing human behaviour." This is not true. We were then and still are producing poor designs because the designers are not aware of the alternatives. Sometimes they are not aware of cheap minor changes that could improve safety at little or no cost. For example, using valves whose position (open or closed) is visible at a glance or using different sorts of hose connectors on compressed air and nitrogen lines, so that they cannot be connected wrongly. Sometimes they are not aware of fundamentally different design options such as inherently safer ones.

I hope these pages will have shown any young engineer or would-be engineer who reads them that life in industry can be absorbing and challenging and that it benefits the community as a whole by providing the wealth necessary for our way of life. It is much more than money making: profit is a measure of our efficiency, not our objective.

ICI's safety inheritance

ICI was formed in 1926 by the amalgamation of four companies and of these Brunner Mond, more than any of the others, set the tone for the new company, partly because Alfred Mond, the son of the founder, Ludwig Mond, was the first chairman. The following quotations from *The Mond Legacy* by Jean Goodman (Wiedenfeld & Nicolson, London, 1982), express a vision and a spirit that was still alive when I retired.

> But Ludwig was not interested in impressing anyone. In the long term he saw himself not as a millionaire, but as a public benefactor who had improved manufacturing processes, saved waste and avoided polluting the countryside. "Our activity acquires an aim as soon as we work for others and every task becomes easy once we undertake it in this spirit", was the pious-sounding philosophy he expressed to Frida (his wife). But beneath the superficial pomposity and smug manner was a true idealism which he never ceased to practice (p24).

In 1874, soon after the start-up of the Winnington factory, a man was killed when a boiler burst.

The death of the workman, however, haunted Ludwig all his life. He saw it as his personal responsibility and never again allowed high-pressure steam to be used in his factories (p41).

Many years later three men employed by the Mond Nickel Company were killed by a leak of carbon monoxide.

He was on holiday in the South of France when he learned of the accident and immediately his mind flashed back more than a quarter of a century to the day when a workman had been scalded to death by an explosion in a boiler plant at Winnington. The thought that he was responsible for the loss of human life was something he could no longer bear. His instinctive reaction was to order the closure of the nickel works and return the shareholders capital from his own pocket. Alfred [his son] was more realistic... (p76)

Early in the war (the 1914-18 war) his firm had realised the imprudence of making TNT in a densely populated area (Silvertown, in the dock area of London) and, as soon as their other works were in full production, had asked to be released from the Silvertown agreement (p101).

Unfortunately the government refused and in 1917 an explosion killed 69 people and injured 400.

Away from work
During my last 10 years or so with ICI my work had been very demanding and during the evenings I was usually reading accident reports in one room while my wife was watching TV in another. Sir Peter Medawar has written (*Advice to a Young Scientist*, Pan Books, London, 1981, p22):

Men or women who go to the extreme length of marrying scientists should be clearly aware beforehand, instead of learning the hard way later, that their spouses are in the grip of a powerful obsession that is likely to take the first place in their lives outside the home, and probably inside too.

This is an extreme view but those who have never been in the grip of such an obsession find it hard to recognise its power. It is not possible to undertake 10% less work and be satisfied with 10% less salary, growth, achievement, responsibility and recognition. The relation between input and results is non-linear.

1980 was not only a year of recession but an unhappy year in other ways. Since late 1979 my wife has been feeling less fit than usual. It gradually got worse and in August 1980 cancer was diagnosed. She was operated on at once but despite chemotherapy she died at the end of October. By this time my sons were grown up. The elder was in his second year at university and the younger in his last year at school. He left for university in the Autumn of 1981 and I rattled around by myself in the family home. But I was away a lot, at Loughborough and elsewhere. In 1985 I moved to the Manchester area to be near my sisters and my mother. She died in 1991 at the age of 99.

My elder son, Anthony, is a chartered accountant and has worked for several companies. He is married with two daughters and lives only an hour's drive away so I am able to see my granddaughters quite frequently. My younger son, Nigel, took a general engineering degree but later moved into purchasing and is now a purchasing officer in a pharmaceutical company.

APPENDIX TO CHAPTER 9

From the *ICI Magazine*, Spring 1985. The words in square brackets were added later.

THE MOND HERITAGE

Looking back, nearly three years after retiring from ICI, I see more clearly than I did then some of its strengths and weaknesses.

1. Jobs are not defined — job descriptions are for assessment, not to tell you what you may and may not do — and therefore one is free within wide limits to expand the scope of one's job. In ICI responsibility is left lying around for anyone who wants to pick it up.

   Of course, there are some things one obviously can do and others one obviously cannot but in between there is a large grey area: if you ask, someone may say no; if you just go ahead, 19 times out of 20, nothing is said. On the twentieth occasion you have got to put up with having your behind kicked. It is not the same in all companies. In a large oil company which I shell, sorry, shall not name, everything seems to be referred to HQ. I have been in meetings with senior people from that company who had no freedom to change their line while more junior ICI men were able, if convinced by the facts or if they considered it expedient, to change their line.

   The disadvantage of the ICI method is that when so much depends on the way the individual does the job, the job may change when he leaves. There is no system, no momentum, to keep things moving when the man who is supplying the drive stops driving. On several occasions valuable procedures have lapsed when the men behind them retired or moved on.

2. ICI people want to get on as much as anyone but there are very, very few people in the company who are prepared to do so at the expense of knocking other people down. In the course of 38 years' service I came across only about three people who were prepared to act in this way.

It may be the same in other large companies, I don't know, I worked only for ICI, but I doubt if it is true in all walks of life. I know of a clergyman, the son of an ICI employee, who says that ICI is a more Christian organization than the Church of England. [An investment manager, writing about the City, says, "The competition between individuals is intense. Most people have neither the time nor any self-interest in offering a helping hand" (Quartano R, *The Chemical Engineer*, October 1988, p68). It was never like that in ICI.]

3. ICI people are not as self-confident as they were when I joined the company. We had no doubt that ICI ways were the best and if those in the outer darkness outside did things differently, that was their misfortune. Then in the 1960s we lost our self-confidence; if we saw other people doing things differently we rushed to copy them — and we have never fully got it back. We were too arrogant in the 1940s and 1950s, we should look at what other people do and be prepared to learn from them, but we should not automatically assume that they are right.

4. ICI has always cared about people and continues to do so, as the article on redeployment in the Autumn 1984 issue shows, but there has been a change. When I joined the company, if someone did not fit he was tried in several jobs and sometimes he was ultimately successful. Now there is a tendency, if a man is not successful in his first job, to label him as useless. Perhaps this is inevitable in a time of recession.

5. When I joined the company it was mainly a company of technologists who made things and somewhere in the background were some commercial people who sold them. The company is now much more market-oriented — it needs to be — but has it gone too far? Is anyone thinking about the technology and where it ought to be going in the way that Bob Malpas and the late Alf Spinks were doing only a few years ago? Someone may be, but if so they are keeping very quiet about it.

Brunner Mond, more than any other of the founder companies, were responsible for the attitudes described above and Winnington Hall where it all started is, I suppose the Jerusalem of ICI.

[Since this was written ICI has sold Winnington Hall.]

10

SECOND CAREER

We caterpillars ... enjoy a privilege unique in nature: To be given our old age first, so that, enriched by the wisdom of experience we may enjoy our youth to the full.

Gilbert Adair, *Alice through the Needle's Eye*
(Pan Books, London, 1985, p148)

fter leaving the life that was past I had a three-month break before reaching the life to come. I spent a month of it in South Africa. After this and later visits one or two people were surprised that I did so. "Was not this", they suggested, "conniving with apartheid?" I asked them who they thought was injured by industrial accidents.

A new life — and a cultural shock

I did not want to move house, and I needed to consult my old ICI files, so I turned the dining room into an office and worked mainly at home. I went down to Loughborough University for a few days at a time every two or three weeks. My lecturing load was light, except when we were running a short course.

Joining the University was a marvellous opportunity as it enabled me to continue to work on the subjects that most interested me. I had colleagues to discuss things with and access to a good library. It was in many ways an idyllic existence and the years at Loughborough were my most productive: five books, about a dozen refereed papers and numerous shorter pieces. I wrote a half-page almost every month for the magazine *Health and Safety at Work* and occasional short items for *The Chemical Engineer*. I doubt if I had any new ideas of any value. I was harvesting the crops sown and nurtured during my time in industry. Of course, in writing my books and papers I had to think my ideas through and develop them. Knowledge remains vague and ill-defined until one has to communicate it. To illustrate my themes, I could draw examples from a large store of notes and memories and I also found new ones, but the essence of what I wrote came from my industrial experience.

How university differed from industry

In several ways joining the University was a cultural shock. There was not a lot of pressure in my ICI job but there was a continuous stream of callers who wanted advice and usually wanted it soon. Much of our self-generated work had to be completed fairly quickly if it was going to have any influence on events. In contrast, in the University nobody seemed to care what I did or when I did it. Of course, I was not involved in university administration, which can be very frustrating, but nevertheless university life would not suit those people who cannot settle down to a job unless they can see a deadline a few days or weeks ahead.

A second difference with industry was the lack of support facilities. I had had a personal secretary, or a share in one, for over twenty years and before that access to typing facilities far better than those available to senior members of the University, eminent in their professions. The girls at Loughborough were all willing and helpful but overworked. No longer could I give a report to my secretary and ask her to send copies to A, B and C. I had to stand at the photocopier and copy it.

The third change I experienced in moving to the University was a drop in contacts. As the reputation of the Group grew, many people from other companies and countries, from universities and government departments, beat a path to our door. Scarcely a week went by without one or more individuals or groups calling on us. Perhaps the word got around official Australian circles that Wilton hospitality was good because one year we had numerous visits from Australian government departments. My knowledge did not leave me the day I left ICI and I expected the stream of visitors to continue, but it did not. Deprived of an official position and the authority that went with it, it was as if I had been unfrocked and lost my powers or, putting it another way, it was ICI the visitors came to consult, not me. To use the metaphor of Romans 11:18, separated from the ICI tree on which I had been grafted, many believed I had no roots to sustain me.

The nature of reputation

Many years ago, as a schoolboy, I read a pamphlet called *Propaganda in International Relations* (Oxford University Press, Oxford, 1939, p26), in which the historian E H Carr argued that propaganda is most effective when those spreading it are seen to hold positions of power. He wrote:

> The almost universal belief in the merits of democracy which spread over the world in 1918 was due less to the inherent excellence of democracy or of the propaganda on its behalf than to the victory of the Allied armies and the Allied blockade. Had the Bolshevik regime collapsed in 1919 far fewer people would today [1939] be convinced of the merits of Marxism.

My experience seems to support this view. Deprived of power, even advisory power, I seemed emasculated and no longer worth consulting. As already mentioned I was allowed to keep an office at Wilton and work on my old files. In exchange, people could pick my brains. Very few did so.

Getting used to it

I do not want to exaggerate. I was committed to the University for four days a week and was involved in a number of committees. I had to turn down much of the consultancy that I was offered. Still I was surprised I did not receive more requests for advice. Gradually my books and papers re-established my reputation in the wider world, the demand for lectures and consultancy grew and since my almost full-time involvement with the University ended I have been offered more work than I have had the time or inclination to accept.

Another surprise I had at the University was the attitude of the students to note-taking. In my undergraduate days we all wrote furiously during lectures, trying to get down as much as possible of the lecturer's words of wisdom, and many of us rewrote our notes afterwards. To my surprise I found that most of today's students just sit back and listen. Anything written on the blackboard or on an overhead projector may be copied but few try to capture the spoken word. Many lecturers give out sets of notes.

The fate of my files

I had a signed agreement with ICI, valid for one year, permitting me to use my old files and an understanding that this would continue for the period of my Loughborough appointment. However, during the first year "There rose a new king who knew not Joseph" (Exodus 1:8). A former Plastics Division man became responsible for production at Wilton. When the agreement was due for renewal I was told it would not be renewed. However, after some correspondence it was agreed that I could visit my old Department to work on my files for five or six days per year. This proved to be sufficient. As time went by I wanted to consult them less and less and in 1985 I left Teesside, thus making further consultation difficult.

My successor, Alan Rimmer, had unfortunately to retire himself in 1983 on health grounds. His successor, Roy Philo, retired in 1986 and the next occupant, my "great-grandson", was moved after two years when there was further consolidation in ICI and Petrochemical and Plastics Division become part of a larger grouping. Much needed continuity was lost. Too frequent movements have always been a feature of ICI. Roy Philo himself had four bosses in two and a half years and the last time I saw him he had difficulty remembering the name of the current incumbent.

Bhopal

My work since leaving ICI has inevitably been influenced by the major accidents of the period. I have described many of them in my book *Learning from Accidents* (2nd edition, Butterworth-Heinemann, Oxford, 1994), with the emphasis on the lessons for the future.

In 1984 the release of toxic vapour at Bhopal, India in 1984 was the worst chemical industry accident ever. It killed over 2000 people. Many things were wrong but most commentators missed the single most important lesson. The substance that leaked, methyl iso-cyanate (MIC), was not a product or raw material but an intermediate. It was convenient to store it but not essential to do so. Afterwards many companies greatly reduced their stocks of MIC and other intermediates, often eliminating them altogether and using the intermediate as soon as it was formed. The worst possible leak was then a few kilograms from a pipeline, not 50 or 100 tonnes from a tank. I had by this time been preaching for ten years that what you don't have can't leak and gradually more people started to listen.

In a way the root cause of Bhopal was hubris. The unspoken assumption of the industry was, "Don't worry about large stocks of hazardous chemicals. We know how to keep them under control". Bhopal almost destroyed that confidence outside the industry but did not weaken it enough within. As a reviewer of *Learning from Accidents* wrote, "It is hubris to imagine we can infallibly prevent a thermo-dynamically favoured event." (Urben P G, *Journal of Loss Prevention in the Process Industries*, Vol 2, No 1, January, 1989, p55)

Nuclear mishaps

Two nuclear accidents, Three Mile Island (1979, while I was still in ICI) and Chernobyl (1986), both had lessons for the chemical industry. Poor training was a feature of both, compounded at Chernobyl by an appalling design, but as at Bhopal there was a lesson that most people missed. There are inherently safer designs of nuclear reactor that are incapable of a runaway reaction or meltdown, not because lots of protective equipment has been added on to prevent it but because the laws of nature make it impossible. In these designs a combination of small size, high heat capacity and ability to withstand high temperature prevents the reactor getting too hot.

There was, however, a feeling among the nuclear establishment in the UK that it had taken them so long to convince Mrs Thatcher and her government to support the Sizewell B design that they felt they would lose credibility if they suggested a new design. There was also a belief that incremental change in existing designs is better than a radically new design which may have unforeseen faults. This sounds convincing until we realise that similar arguments could have been (and probably were) used in the early 19th century to advocate the breeding of better horses instead of building railway locomotives. The problems of horses were well-understood and much money had already been invested in their breeding.

Piper Alpha

In 1988 167 people were killed by the fire and explosion on the Piper Alpha oil platform in the North Sea. I felt this was where I came in. Like the 1967 fire at North Tees that led to my appointment (see page 78), it was due to poor practice in the preparation of equipment for maintenance, not so much poor instructions but a failure to follow them. A piece of equipment was brought back into use before maintenance was complete. Senior managers had not noticed that the practice was slack or they had turned a blind eye. Similar incidents continue to occur throughout industry. Frank Lees was one of the technical assessors to the chairman of the Piper Alpha inquiry and another was a former colleague from my Oil Works days, Brian Appleton.

Writing

During my first year at Loughborough I prepared a collection of accident reports from my *Safety Newsletters* for publication. ICI generously raised no objection. The reports were chosen as typical of those that occur in the chemical industry and emphasise the action to be taken to prevent them happening again. I had to rewrite most of the *Newsletter* reports in order to achieve a continuity of style; I could not prepare the book with scissors and paste. I chose an American publisher, Gulf, partly because they wooed me assiduously and partly because the US market is so much bigger than the UK market. The book *What Went Wrong?* has sold well as technical books go: over 14,000 copies.

While I was writing *What Went Wrong?* I also started on what became a series of four paperbacks for the Institution of Chemical Engineers. They were all re-issued as hardbacks and are now in their 3rd or 4th editions. The first of these books, *Hazop and Hazan — Identifying and Assessing Chemical Industry Hazards* was based on lecture notes I had used for several years and describes hazard and operability studies (Hazop) and hazard analysis (Hazan). It is intended for those new to the subjects and is not a manual for experts. Unlike many books on the subject, it spends more time on examples, pitfalls and limitations than on complex mathematics that is rarely used in practice.

The second book was originally called *Cheaper, Safer Plants*. The latest edition is called *Process Plants: A Handbook for Inherently Safer Design* (2nd edition, Taylor & Francis, Philadelphia, PA, 1998). It describes the concepts of inherently safer design and simpler plants, sometimes called friendly plants, with many examples of their application. The original title was chosen to draw attention to the fact that inherently safer designs are usually cheaper, for two reasons: we do not need so much added-on safety equipment and, if we can reduce the amount of material in the plant, the equipment will be smaller and therefore cheaper.

The third book, now called *Dispelling Chemical Engineering Myths* (3rd edition, Taylor & Francis, London and Philadelphia, PA, 1996), describes a number of widely held but incorrect beliefs, some technical, some managerial, and some of the incorrect actions taken as a result.

The fourth book, *An Engineer's View of Human Error*, discusses accidents which at first sight seem to be due to human error but which could be prevented by changing the plant design or methods of operation (including training and auditing). The theme of the book is that it is difficult to prevent people making errors and so we should try to remove opportunities for errors and error-prone situations. When I was an assistant works manager the company's official statistics showed that most accidents were due to human failing. I wrote to the then company safety adviser to say that my experience showed that all but a few of our accidents could have been prevented, or made less likely, by management action of some sort and that it was hard to believe that we were different from other works.

More books

When the Science and Engineering Research Council grant ended I was awarded a Leverhulme Trust Emeritus Fellowship that allowed me to continue at the University for another two years. After that I became a freelance consultant and writer but have kept a foot in the door at Loughborough as a Senior Visiting Research Fellow ever since.

During these later years, besides new editions of my early books, I produced several more. *Critical Aspects of Safety and Loss Prevention*

(Butterworths, 1990) was a sort of abc of safety and loss prevention, a series of short articles on hundreds of topics, arranged alphabetically.

Learning from Accidents (2nd edition, Butterworth-Heinemann, 1994) considers about twenty accidents in detail, looking not only for the immediate technical causes but for weakness in management and the ways in which the hazard might have been avoided. The accidents include well-known one such as Seveso, Piper Alpha and Chernobyl, some railway disasters and others not well-known that display important messages.

Lessons from Disaster — How Organisations have No Memory and Accidents Recur describes accidents that have occurred again because the lessons of the past were forgotten and suggests ways of improving the corporate memory. As mentioned in Chapter 7, while looking for old accident reports in ICI's files I had found a report on a very similar accident to the one at North Tees in 1967 (see Chapters 6 and 7) that led to my appointment. The 1969 Polythene Plant explosion (Chapter 7) was similar in many ways to the one that had occurred in Oil Works 12 years earlier (Chapter 4). Many other examples came to light. Only people have memories and ten years after a serious incident there are few people still around who remember what happened and the reasons why procedures were introduced. Someone keen to improve efficiency asks, "Why are we using this time-consuming method?" No-one knows, the procedure is abandoned, or allowed to lapse, and the accident it was designed to prevent happens again.

Computer Control and Human Error (Institution of Chemical Engineers, Rugby, UK, 1995) was written with two Loughborough colleagues, Paul Chung and Eamon Broomfield, and an Israeli friend, Chaim Shen-Orr. It describes many computer failures and suggests how they might be avoided. When I left ICI computer control was just coming into widespread use. There had been a few incidents as a result but nothing serious and I wanted to learn from them before more serious ones occurred. The commonest cause of problems was poor understanding between the software engineers and their clients. The software engineers did not fully understand what the plant designers and operators wanted and the operators did not understand the limitations of what they got.

All these books have a feature in common: I start with accident reports and draw the messages — the lists of what we should and should not do — out of them. Many writers do the reverse: they start with the codes and recommended practices and show how failures to follow them have resulted or will result in accidents. I prefer my approach, for two reasons.

First, accident reports grab our attention and we read on (or pay attention if someone is talking). In contrast, codes and standards are put aside to read when we have time, and we all know what that means. They are usually a turn-off.

Second, the accident is the important bit. It tells us what happened. You may not agree with the code or standard but you can't deny that the accident happened. You may not agree with some (or even all) of the advice in my books but I hope you won't disregard the accident reports. If you don't like my advice, I hope you will decide what to do instead.

More travel and consultancy

I continued to travel a good deal after leaving ICI and have attended conferences and companies in many countries. I am one of those parodied by David Lodge in *Small World* (Penguin, London, 1985):

> The modern conference resembles the pilgrimage of medieval Christendom in that it allows the participants to indulge themselves in all the pleasures and diversions of travel while appearing to be austerely bent on self-improvement. To be sure there are certain penitential exercises to be performed — the presentation of a paper, perhaps, and certainly listening to the papers of others. But with this excuse you journey to new and interesting places, meet new and interesting people... eat, drink and make merry in their company every evening; and yet, at the end of it all, return home with an enhanced reputation for seriousness of mind.

In 1986 I received the Bill Doyle Award of the American Institute of Chemical Engineers for the best paper presented at the 1985 Loss Prevention Symposium. It was on inherently safer design. The year before, the first time it was awarded, the winner was Jim McQuaid, so there was a double recognition of my old department. I received several more awards in the following years, including several from the

Institution of Chemical Engineers. My most unexpected award, however, was being elected a Fellow of the Fellowship of Engineering (now the Royal Academy of Engineering) in 1984. At the time membership was restricted to a thousand and for a chemist to be elected a Fellow was an honour indeed.

Another surprise honour was being appointed an Officer of the Order of the British Empire in 1997.

My consultancy has been mainly one or two-day stands: giving a talk to a company safety conference, having a look round a plant and commenting on what I saw, advising on a specific problem. I have had a few longer jobs: advising on a litigation case or assisting in the preparation of a report. I have had only one continuing assignment: the Health and Safety Executive suggested to a company that they should have an outsider on the safety committee at each of their sites and I agreed to serve on one of them.

At first I was disappointed. The committee discussed policy rather than accidents, what they called the helicopter view. It seemed to me that one can't understand the view from a helicopter unless one lands it and samples the detail and it took a while before I found out how to do this — that is, to get hold of accident reports, visit the site of them, discuss them with some of the people involved and comment on them at the meetings.

My old company

Since I left ICI I have watched with mixed feelings the changes it has undergone, far greater than those that took place during my 38 years there. Many have been typical of industry as a whole (demanning, outsourcing, concentration on core businesses, less job security, units changing their owners more often than some people change their underclothing) but in ICI the core has changed. Virtually all the plants on the Billingham and Wilton sites have been sold and the proceeds used to buy speciality chemical plants, mainly from Unilever. By moving away from bulk chemicals, the company hopes that there will be fewer ups and downs in sales and profits. In addition, the pharmaceuticals and related businesses (a third of the capital but two-thirds of the profits) were demerged as Zeneca, now part of AstraZeneca. ICI is now like a hammer that has been in continuous use for 75 years but has during that time needed a new head and a new handle.

Another change has been to bring in people from outside for the top jobs in the company. In the past ICI bred its own leaders. There was no shortage of talent. As I pointed out in Chapter 1, four former colleagues of mine have been knighted. Other colleagues, good steady people who did a sound job and earned their keep but would never have got very far in ICI, have left the company and done well elsewhere. Have recruitment standards fallen or has the company lost confidence in itself? I do not know.

ICI today is not much bigger than Petrochemicals Division in its prime. The individual businesses are, and should be, responsible for safety but, I have been told, no-one is now providing the sort of technical oversight and guidance that I tried to provide.

Some final thoughts

- There is a welcome interest today in safety management systems but we must not forget their limitations. Some managers seem to think that a good management system will produce a safe plant. This is not so. As mentioned at the beginning of Chapter 2, all that a system can do is harness the knowledge and experience of people. If knowledge and experience have been downsized away, the system is an empty shell. Knowledge and experience without a system will achieve less than their full potential. Without knowledge and experience a system will achieve nothing.

  To quote a reviewer of one of my books, "Overall, there is a constant underlying message within this book that pervades every page, section and chapter. The technique of Hazop and Hazan requires total commitment by management, and knowledgeable and experienced people to carry it out. In reading this book, it became very apparent that the technique is extremely powerful, but that power can only be realised by having the right people present when it is undertaken." (Astbury G, *The Chemical Engineer*, No 689, 7 October 1999, p34) The same applies to all the loss prevention techniques.

- In every walk of life, if comments are based, as mine are, on past experience, someone will say, "Schools/hospitals/offices/factories aren't like that any more." Is old information still relevant? In many ways factories, at least, ARE like they used to be as human nature is a common factor. We may have better equipment but we may be just as likely as in the past to cut corners when we design, construct, operate, test and maintain it — perhaps more likely, as there are fewer of us to keep our eyes open as we go round the plant and follow up unusual observations. We may have access to more knowledge than our parents and grandparents, but are we any more thorough and reliable?

- I have worked in industry as a line manager with the authority, in theory, to impose my views and as an adviser who can only persuade. If one can give people the skill and knowledge to decide for themselves what is safe (empower them in today's management jargon), then their convictions will survive after one has left, they will have become second nature. In contrast, practices imposed by authority lapse when the boss moves on or, more often, when the boss loses interest.

- Some writers seem to think that accidents occur because directors and senior managers are hard-nosed and uncaring people interested only in profit and unconcerned about safety. This is not so. They genuinely want safer plants but many do not realise that they could do more. They do not realise that taking an interest in the lost-time accident rate is not sufficient. In high-technology industries it may be counter-productive as it indicates to their staff that they are not aware of the real problems. They do not identify the precise actions required, see that they are carried out and monitor progress.

- I never had any formal training in safety, and this was in many ways an advantage as I had few pre-conceived ideas. Job training is on balance a good thing but it can produce clones of the trainer and this can inhibit new ideas. I was fortunate not to be inhibited in this way. "Absence of baggage from the past gives people the freedom to ask awkward questions and not to reject ideas because they know someone has tried them before" (Denyer R, *Chemistry and Industry* — *Supplement*, November 1999, p2).

- We interpret what we read and hear against a background of pre-conceived ideas. Within our own organisation we know the background and present our arguments accordingly. Talking to an outside group is harder as we don't know the background and may try to convince people of views they already take for granted, or take for granted views they do not accept.

Sadly, Frank Lees, nine years younger than me, died in 1999. His contribution to loss prevention was immense. His major achievement was his monumental *Loss Prevention in the Process Industries* (Butterworth-Heinemann, Oxford, 2nd edition, 1996, 3 volumes) but he also carried out an extensive programme of research, trained many students and wrote numerous papers.

I never saw him angry, frustrated or excited. He was a very private man who kept his feelings to himself. He gave up much of his time to public service, including the two years he spent as one of the technical assessors to the Piper Alpha inquiry.

When his illness was diagnosed and he was given two years to live he was remarkably composed. He finished and wrote up his outstanding work and calmly waited for the end. One test of a man is: did he make full use of his ability? Frank had a lot of ability and used it to the full. His friends, colleagues and students will remember him as someone who lived a full life with integrity and industry and set an example to us all. I was lucky to work with him.

The years since my full-time involvement at Loughborough have been busy ones, full of interest and free from stress — otherwise I would not have gone on working — but there are no major new initiatives to describe. The accidents of the period have re-enforced old messages, not taught us new ones. I have continued to work on much the same themes as I did in ICI. These are summarised in Table 10.1 (on the next page) together with the problems and events that sent me in those directions. I am not and never will be at the end of the road.

The day is short and the work is great and the Master of the house is urgent. It is not your duty to finish the work but neither are you free to desist from it.

Sayings of the Fathers, 3rd century AD

Hazop	The obvious need to find out what can go wrong without waiting unit it has gone wrong. Hazop is the preferred technique for the process industries.
Hazan (QRA)	The need to set priorities. We need a defensible method of deciding which hazards to remove or reduce first, which to leave alone, at least for the time being, what risks are intolerable and what are acceptable.
Inherently safer design	Flixborough (and then Bhopal) made us realise what should have been obvious: it is better to remove a hazard than to keep it under control. What you don't have can't leak. We can't fall down stairs that aren't there.
Preparation for maintenance	The fire in 1967 which was due to poor procedures for the preparation of equipment for repair. It made ICI realise that safety advisers should have experience of the technology.
Control of modifications	Flixborough (and other less serious incidents).
A new attitude to human error	The realisation that most accidents could be prevented (or made less likely) by managers' actions. To say accidents are due to human failing is true but is as helpful as saying that falls are due to gravity.
Better investigation of accidents	The realisation that many accident investigations are superficial, dealing only with the immediate causes and not looking for ways of avoiding the hazard or for weaknesses in management.
Better publicity for accident reports	For four reasons: (a) moral (b) so that others will tell us about their accidents (c) so that they will make the changes we make and (d) because in the eyes of the public the industry is one.
Better ways of remembering the lessons of the past	Both major and minor accidents are repeated after a few years, even in the same organisation.
Audits and inspections	Outsiders can spot hazards that we do not see as the hazards are too familiar or we lack the time or specialised knowledge.
Myths of the chemical industry	We all accept unthinkingly beliefs that are not wholly true and can lead to accidents and wrong decisions.
Accident case histories	The realisation that (a) case histories grab our attention much more effectively than advice and (b) people may not agree with my advice but they can hardly ignore the accidents. We should start with the accidents and draw the lessons out of them.

Table 10.1 WHAT I DID AND WHY I DID IT
My main interests in loss prevention and what triggered them

INDEX

A

accepted wisdom, 14-15, 46-47
accident reports
    avoiding superficiality in 44-45, 81-82, 84
    features of 133
    publication 85, 109-110, 130
accidents
    early 36, 44-45, 51-52
    fatal 62-65, 74, 78, 82-85, 119
    investigation of 81, 132
    repeated 80-81, 111-112, 132
    statistics 68-69, 74, 119
    welfare of the injured 65
    see also fire, explosion
Acetone Plant 30-34, 37, 44
achievements 119, 138
Adair, Gilbert 113-114, 125
Allen, Sir Peter 9
amateurism 84-85
ammonia synthesis 12-13, 18, 51
Angus, Tommy 24
Appleton, Brian 130
atomic bombs 4, 6
"autumn flowers" 88
awards 133-134

B

batch processes 35, 102
Beaumont, Stanley 107

Bell, Douglas, 39
Bhopal 83, 102, 128-129
Billingham site 5, 7, 10, 41, 56, 84-85, 134
Birchall, Derek 77-78
bonus schemes 28, 71-73
Booker, Bert 49-50, 53, 59
Boycott, Mike 49
Bosanquet, C H 10
Bradford, Bernard 14, 16
British Association 117
Brunner Mond 120-121, 124

C

Cambridge 8
Capa, Robert 89
carbonylation 48-50, 60
career, choice of 2, 5, 113-114
carbon monoxide 10-11, 121
change
    attitudes to 27, 50
    unforeseen results of 44-45
Challis, Edward 49-50, 53, 59-61, 77, 98, 100, 110-111, 113-116
chargehands 11, 24
chemical engineering 22, 39, 47, 50, 114
chemists, what they have to learn 21, 39
Chernobyl 129, 132
Chester 1, 4

G

H

I

J

K

Kantyka, Ted 94, 114

L

labour relations 4, 27-28, 54-56, 71-75
Lamb, Sydney 87, 106
Lawley, Bert, 90, 99, 106
leaks 44-45, 82-85
Lees, David 14-16
Lees, Frank 114, 118, 130, 137
legislation on safety 87-88
lions and lambs 102
liquefied flammable gases 88
Liverpool University 4, 7-8
lobbying, need for 24-28
Lodge, David 133
Loughborough University 114, 118, 125-128, 131

M

MacDonald, Ramsey 18
maintenance, preparation for 78-80, 84-85
Malpas, Sir Robert (Bob) 7, 26, 103, 124
"manageers" 22, 72
management
    by persuasion 24, 89, 136
    change, effects of 59-61
    reasons for poor 97-98
    responsibilities 29-30, 37, 60-61, 77
    science 68

systems, 7, 135
training, superficial 68-69, 92
McQuaid, Jim 105-106, 134
Medawar, Sir Peter 14, 121-122
"minimum capital cost" 58
Mitchell, Frank 106
modifications, see change
Mond, Alfred 120-121
Mond, Ludwig 120-121
Montefiore, Sir Moses 3
myths 131

N

naphtha 51-52
"near misses" 110-111
nitrogen blanketing 65-67
nitroglycerine manufacture 31-32, 95, 101
North, Harry 47, 68
North Tees Works 41, 51-52, 55, 73, 78-81, 86, 130
nuclear reactors 129-130
numerical problem-solving 25, 98-99
Nylon Works 58, 84-85, 90, 96-97, 99

O

Oil Works 18-37, 46-75
Olefine Works 19, 39, 41-42, 47-49, 53
one-legged stools 31, 95
organisational problems 48-49, 52-53

P

Palmer, "Nylon" 46-47
para-xylene 39
Parvin, Ron 106
pay and conditions 11-12
petrol production 18-19, 21
Phenol Plants 51, 58
Philo, Roy 128
photographing hazards 67-68, 81
Piper Alpha 130, 132
Polythene Plant explosion 82-83, 99
pollution, early attitudes 36
Price, Bill 7-8, 10, 13, 15, 20, 29, 50, 61
problems, numerical treatment of 25, 98-99
process investigation 46-47, 61
productivity 28, 71-75
programmed decisions 26, 35
propylene leak and fire 44-45
protective equipment, inspection of 66
publications 98, 111, 113, 130-133
Pugh, Alan 88

Q

quality (of workmanship) 15
quantitative risk analysis 98-99

R

Ramsgate 3
Ramshaw, Colin 101

rates of pay 11, 28, 58
  assessment of 91-93
recession 116
relief valves, leaking 25
re-organisation 42-43, 90, 96-97, 117, 134-135
reputation 126-127
research 6-10, 13-16
  "hands-on" 14
resources, finding 106-107
responsibilities 72, 77, 123
retirement 116-118
risks compared 117
Rhyl 3
Rimmer, Alan 118, 128
Roeber, Joe 53, 72
Roesler, Frank 40
Robertson, Alan 26
Rotblat, Joseph 4

S

safety
  attitudes towards 35-36, 73-74, 119-121
  experience grows 62-67
  legislation on 87-88
  start of interest in 35-36, 44-45, 61-64
  surveys 86-87
safety adviser 76-90, 94-122
  job guidelines 76-78
Safety Newsletter 77, 108-111
school 1-2
scientific ladder 113
Seneca xv
Senior Training Corps 4